W9-BOK-148

WITHDRAWN

70-781

VM
363
C33

Cagle
Flying ships.

Date Due JUL   2000

			2000
		JUN	2004
		JUN 09	
		JUL X X 2015	

PRINTED IN U.S.A.

WITHDRAWN

FLYING SHIPS
Hovercraft and Hydrofoils

Rear Admiral
Malcolm W. Cagle, U.S.N.

FLYING SHIPS
Hovercraft and Hydrofoils

Illustrated with Photographs

CUMBERLAND COUNTY COLLEGE
LIBRARY P.O. BOX 517 VINELAND N.J.

DODD, MEAD & COMPANY
New York

VM
363
C 33

70-781

CREDITS FOR PHOTOGRAPHS

Aero-Go Company, Inc., Seattle, Washington, 65, 82, 83, 84; Aerojet General Corporation, 100; Airavia, Ltd., Isle of Wight, England, 110; Anglican Development Ltd., Isle of Wight, 115; Melville Beardsley, 18, 19, 70; Behlen Manufacturing Company, Columbus, Nebraska, 87; Dr. William R. Bertelsen, 24; Bertin & Cie, France, 93; Boeing Company, 113; Booz-Allen and The U.S. Maritime Administration, 125; British Hovercraft Corporation, Ltd., 15, 26, 27, 58, 61 118, (bottom); British Information Services, Central Office of Information, London, 55 (top), 77, 78, 80; Walter A. Crowley, 23; Denny Hovercraft, Ltd., London, 59; Franklin A. Dobson, 20, 21, 64; Mr. A. B. German, President, Hoverwork Canada Ltd., and Briston Films, Ltd., 57; The Gunderson Corporation, 88 (bottom); Hover-Air Ltd., England, 67; Hovermarine, Ltd., Southampton, England, 99, 118 (top), 126; Hoverwork, Canada, Ltd., 90; Alex Jardine, 73; Ralph Maloof of Cushion Flight Company, 66; National Geographic Society, Gilbert H. Grosvenor, 106; National Physical Laboratory-Hovercraft Unit, Southampton, England, 29, 85; Science Museum, South Kensington, London, 13; "Seattle Times" Co., Seattle, Washington, 88 (top); SEDAM, Paris, 91, 92; Supramar, Switzerland, 111; Textron's Bell Aerosystems Company, 37 (top), 49, 50, 52, 101, 120, 121, 123 (bottom); U.S. Army Photograph, Courtesy of Lt. Col. Jim I. Hunt, 44; U.S. Maritime Commission, 123 (top); U.S. Navy Photograph, 37 (bottom), 41, 97, 98; U.S. Navy Photograph, Courtesy of Lt. Kenneth E. Luenser, 40; Vosper Ltd., Portsmouth, England, 55 (bottom); Wynne-Gill Associates, Inc., 114.

Copyright © 1970 by Rear Admiral M. W. Cagle, U.S.N.
All rights reserved
No part of this book may be reproduced in any form without permission in writing from the publisher
Library of Congress Catalog Card Number: 77-111910
Printed in the United States of America

THE OPINIONS or assertions in this book are the personal ones of the author and are not to be construed as official. They do not necessarily reflect the views of either the Navy Department or the Department of Defense.

Acknowledgments

This project was undertaken as an off-hours, self-educational task to examine in depth the new ideas and concepts of hovercraft and hydrofoils as they may possibly affect the U.S. Navy of the next decade. When the wartime problems of the Gulf of Tonkin and the Sea of Japan became too intense, the author could always mentally escape into a futuristic marine world for a relaxing hour or two.

I have had abundant and enthusiastic help from the following people, and I list their names with gratitude:

Melville A. Beardsley, Dr. William R. Bertelsen, JOCS Richard A. Carlson, USN, Harvey B. Chaplin, Sir Christopher Cockerell, Walter A. Crowley, Franklin A. Dobson, Jan A. Eglen, CAPT Roy Faulk, USN, Peter G. Fielding, Vice President and Director of Research, Booz Allen Applied Research, A. B. German, Percy Hicks, LCOL Jim I. Hunt, USA, Alex M. Jardine, Frank F. Kulik, LT Kenneth H. Luenser, USN, Ralph P. Maloof, President, Cushion Flight Corp., PHC Virgil O. McColley, USN, LT Lloyd McIntyre, USN, MAJ David G. Moore, USA, YNC John L. Murray, USN, W. B. Nixon, Marvin Pitkin, Ralph Schneider, David G. M. Scott, CAPT W. E. Webber, USN, K. G. Wood, General Manager, Aero-Go, Inc.

Author's Foreword and Dedication

This book is written to explain the potential and promise of ships that fly—the special effects ships, hovercraft, air cushion vehicles, hydrofoils, and captured air bubble craft which will play an increasingly important role in the field of ocean travel and transportation, sporting and naval affairs over the next quarter century. It is particularly directed to those young people who are at the point of choosing their career and life's work.

Besides telling the story of these "flying ships," however, this book has two key lessons. First, that new ideas—*really* new ideas, the ones that are novel and original—are as unique and rare as large diamonds. Men who produce such ideas are few and far between, and most of them are dreamers—men not usually able to translate their ideas into reality or to articulate them to others. (A correlary of this important lesson is that the rest of us who depend on the forward-looking ideas of others are often incapable of recognizing the value of such ideas when they are presented. Usually we scoff or are skeptical or we keep an ignorant silence.)

So it was with air cushion vehicles (ACV's) and the surface effects ships (SES's). The *idea* is at least 100 years old—perhaps even more. The earliest record of the air cushion vehicle was one devised by a Swedish philosopher and scientist named Swedenborg. He demonstrated a model, which was worked by pedals and a pump, in 1716. In 1912, in Western Australia, A. V. Adcock demonstrated the ACV principle with a simple wooden model. This consisted of a four-foot square, two-inch thick platform, on which was mounted an electric motor driving a compressor and propeller. In 1939, he made a similar demonstration in England. But no one recognized the value of the ACV idea at that time.

As for the hydrofoil, the idea goes back more than sixty-five years. Among the first people who worked on it were the Wright Brothers and Alexander Graham Bell. Yet the hydrofoil did not come into reality until the 1950's.

Those who invented the original ideas for the hovercraft and the captured air bubble ship during the last two centuries, as well as those who heard about or saw demonstrations of those original ideas, did not know what they were hearing or seeing and did not appreciate their potentials. And so, the hovercraft and the captured air bubble ship ideas were germinated in the nineteenth century, but died, were re-born in the 1880–1930 period, and died again—until the late 1950's.

The point is—people with good ideas must be able to communicate and articulate them to others in order to bring them into practical reality. Also, those who encounter them for the first time must be sufficiently open-minded to appreciate their potential—otherwise, the good ideas may become merely sterile and futile mental gymnastics. Representatives of these diverse fields of dreamers and doers must look across the bridges in between and cooperate to achieve their worthwhile concrete goals. So it was with hovercraft. It was Cockerell the radio engineer, Beardsley the Air Force officer, Bertelsen the physician, and Chaplin the aerodynamic mathematician whose ideas and ingenuity were combined to produce this distinctive and new type of transport—just as it was the bicycle makers, Orville and Wilbur Wright, who made the first practical airplane.

It is to you effectively cooperating people—the new idea generators, the new idea developers—that this book is respectfully dedicated.

Rear Admiral, U.S. Navy

Gulf of Tonkin
31 May 1969
USS Enterprise

Contents

FLYING SHIPS
Hovercraft and Hydrofoils

1

What Is "It"?

It was only a few years ago—1959—that the first air cushion vehicle journey was undertaken. Ever since that time, there has been a lively debate about what these craft are, and how they should be designated.

Sir Christopher Cockerell once jokingly called his invention "a very expensive motor car with a permanent puncture."

"It" is not a helicopter—although it *does* hover like one. "It" is not a ship—but it *does* go over the sea. "It" is not an airplane—but it does "fly." Some "its" are pure marine craft and never navigate away from the water. Others are true amphibians and operate both on land and in the water. The truth is, "it" is all of these things —helicopter, airplane, ship—and yet *none* of them.

So what is "it"?

One of our first tasks in answering this question is to straighten out the varied and confusing terminology which surrounds words like "hovercraft," "PAK-V" and "hydroskimmer," and cryptic initials like ACV, GEM, TAC, CAB, SEV, and SES.

Most writers describe "it" by using such words as vehicle, craft, gadget, machine, or thing—and avoid using airplane, helicopter, boat, or similar designations. In truth, the "its" are the newest and most novel man-made machines which can travel over land and water, swamps and rice paddies, marshes and mud banks, ice and snow, tidal streams and canals—lakes and rivers, at least *some* of them can! Still others, the Captured Air Bubble, the hybrid hovercraft and hydrofoils, are meant only for ocean travel.

Let us begin by omitting the hydrofoils—ships that fly *in* the water—until we get to Chapter 11.

The most graphic of the many abbreviations, perhaps, is SES—surface effect ship—if the word "ship" is understood to include something (not an airplane) that travels in the air over any surfaces, liquid or solid. In this sense, one type of SES is the "hovercraft." This term, derived, of course, from the verb "hover," is the creation of the recognized inventor of hovercraft, Sir Christopher S. Cockerell.

But does "it" actually fly? The United States Federal Aviation Agency, when it was asked to rule about an experimental hovercraft commuter service, sidestepped the question by replying that "it" did not come under that Agency's regulations. The International Civil Aeronautical Organization (ICAO) says "it" is that hovercraft are vehicles in their own right. So the answer is—"it" *does* fly; but "it" is *not* an airplane.

At first, the word "hovercraft" was registered, so several other terms in addition to the preferred SES, came into usage—ACV (Air Cushion Vehicle); GEM (Ground Effect Machine); GERM (Ground Effect Research Machine) and SEV (Surface Effect Vessel); CAB (Captured Air Bubble); TAC (Trapped Air Cushion); and PACV (a U.S. naval term meaning Patrol Air Cushion Vehicle).

Whatever they are called, the "its" are unique in origin. The ship, for example, came from some primitive man who watched a log floating down a river, then got the idea of hollowing out a tree to make the world's first boat. The automobile is an adaptation of the wheel—and the wheel was created when some primitive man, thousands of years ago, observed a log rolling down a mountain, sawed off two sections, fastened one on either side of a big box in such a manner that it would rotate, and made himself a cart. The airplane, of course, came from man watching the birds fly, and yearning for centuries to imitate them. Finally he built himself wings and an engine powerful enough to conquer his weight.

But the "its" imitate nothing in nature, either in performance or principle. They are a product of lively imagination, skilled technology, and tireless laboratory experiment. They are the only unique form of transportation to be developed in half a century.

In simplest terms, the "its" are man-made machines, supported mainly by a cushion of air trapped between the base of the vehicle and the surface over which it is operating.

There are two principal types of "it": *flexible sidewalls* (which have skirts) and *fixed sidewalls* (which have solid sides). The former can be amphibious and operated over any terrain, whereas the fixed sidewalls are purely marine vessels.

The "its" have also accumulated a variety of nicknames—"flying saucers" was an obvious first. "PAK-V" is another term used by U.S. Navy sailors; also "monster," a nickname derived from wartime experience in Southeast Asia, because the enemy Viet Cong called "it" *Quai Vat,* their Vietnamese words meaning "monster." In the U.S. Army, the GI's call them "Charlie Victors"—cushion vehicles. Writers have used such words as "skimmers," "flying carpets," "waterbugs," "hydrokeels" and "cushioncraft."

As indicated previously, for the purpose of simplification in this book, I have selected the most graphic symbol, SES—surface effect ship—as the generic term for flying ships, with ACV and hovercraft understood to cover *flexible skirt amphibious craft,* and CAB to include the *seagoing, waterborne, and fixed sidewall ship.*

The SES Principle

Here is a brief description of what an SES is and how it functions.

As has been stated above, there are two main types of SES craft: (1) the Flexible Skirt craft (which include GEM's, Hovercraft,

ACV's, and Peripheral Jets); and (2) the Fixed Sidewalls or Captured Air Bubble (CAB) ships. SES can be two distinct types: (1) an aerodynamic SES, and (2) an aerostatic SES. An aerodynamic SES moves through the air and its shape produces lift, just as the wing moving through air lifts an aircraft. In the aerostatic SES, the pressure of air underneath the vessel lifts it out of the water or clear of the surface. It is this second type which we will discuss.

Both types of SES—fixed wall or flexible wall—have one thing in common—their weight is supported, in whole or in part, by air pressure, trapped by some means beneath them.

Figure 1 will illustrate why surface effect ships, either flexible wall or fixed wall, have a potential advantage over conventional ships.

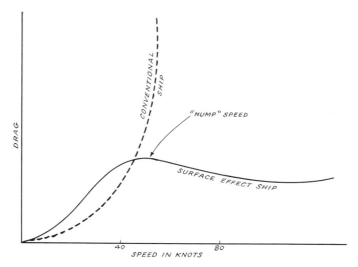

Speed advantage of a Surface Effect Ship

It is easy to see that, as the speed of a conventional ship increases, the drag, or water resistance, increases rapidly. In fact, shipbuilders consider that the practical speed limit of the traditional hulled ship is about 35-40 knots. Even for a specially designed nuclear power submarine, the top speed is approximately 50 knots. Above these speeds, the horsepower required (and the associated expense of building and operating such ships) increases so rapidly as to make more horsepower prohibitive in cost.

The two major types of surface effect ships, however, have a significant advantage over the ordinary ship, once they get above the "hump" speed, defined just below. This is partly because as soon as the SES starts riding on an air cushion, the latter causes a "hole" or depression in the water below it equal to its own displacement. As the SES increases its forward speed, the hole in the water under the craft moves forward and produces waves, just like an ordinary ship makes waves. But as its speed is increased still further, the SES craft climbs on top of its bow wave and begins to "plane." At this point, called the "hump" speed, the wave-making drag is reduced and the SES accelerates still further. Thus, as Figure 1 shows, the drag is *decreased*, the speed is *increased*, and the SES can go to higher speeds *without any increase in installed power*.

Since water is about 815 times denser than air, it is obviously easier and less expensive to push a ship through *air* than through *water*.

In Figure 2, it can be seen that the total drag, or resistance, to a

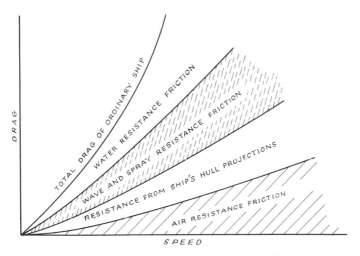

Four types of drag on a conventional ship

conventional ship being pushed through the water is made up of four different kinds:

- The water resistance itself.
- The resistance from any waves or spray through which the ship is moving.
- The resistance caused by any projections which stick out of the hull into the water (such as scoops, propeller struts, fittings, even barnacles).
- Wind and air resistance.

For the SES, the first three are greatly minimized—the water resistance, the wave resistance, and the hull projections. This allows the SES, while using the same amount of power, to go much faster than the conventional ship.

In examining the SES craft themselves, we will begin with the simple air cushion vehicle (ACV), one of several "flexible wall" ships.

As will be described in the next chapter, the inventors soon discovered that the simplest ACV type is the one shown in Figure 3, commonly called the *Open Plenum* type ACV.

By means of a fan, or propeller, fitted in the top of the craft, air is forced beneath the hull and allowed to escape. When the air pressure beneath the craft is sufficient, it is lifted from the surface, and air escapes around the lower edges. In this open plenum chamber type, the "flexible" wall or skirt is simply an "air" skirt.

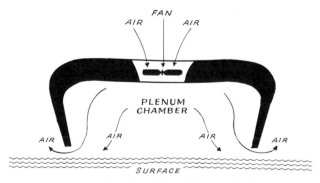

Bow view of an Open Plenum Craft

But this simple open plenum has several disadvantages. First of all, the hovering height can only be a matter of inches. Therefore, the open plenum chamber SES can only clear obstacles or waves which are very low and small. Second, a large amount of power is needed to move the necessary volume of air. Third, such a simple craft normally requires two power sources if it is to travel—one power source to *lift* the craft, another to *move* it. For these reasons, the plenum chamber is not efficient. It certainly isn't the way to make boats go *faster*.

But even this relatively inefficient system has led to some useful applications. The Hoover Vacuum Cleaning Company, for example, used this system for its "floating" vacuum cleaner, making it easy for a housewife to move her cleaner from one room to another. Also, a refrigerator manufacturer uses this system to provide an easy way to "float" his equipment away from the wall (employing a vacuum cleaner attachment which blows air beneath the base of the refrigerator), so that the floor under it can be cleaned.

The second type of ACV is called the peripheral jet. (Figure 4). In this type, a curtain of continuous jets of air is ejected downward and *inward* from around the periphery of the craft (hence the name peripheral jet). The cushion pressure, acting on the bottom area of the craft, produces a greater upward force than in the simple open plenum type. In fact, this design will permit a power reduction of about 50 per cent to achieve the same amount of clearance above

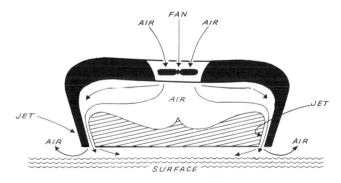

Peripheral Jet SES

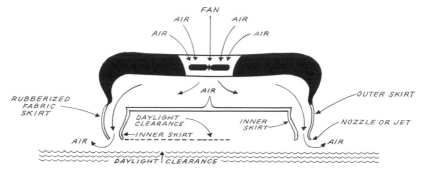

Flexible Skirt Craft

the surface.

In other words, the air jets produce an air "curtain," trapping compressed air beneath the craft more effectively than is the case with the open plenum type, and preventing its escape. Most important, the clearance above the surface may be many times higher for the same amount of installed power.

It was essentially this peripheral jet system which was used by the first ACV to cross the English Channel successfully in July 1959— the SR.N1 described in Chapter 3.

However, with all the added improvements, the peripheral jets, with only air curtains, are still not able to cross high obstacles or the large waves that are common on the open seas, even in good weather.

It was this problem which finally led to the idea of using rubberized fabric skirts, or flexible extensions.

Figure 5 shows the basic design of a flexible skirt craft.

Flexible Skirts

Since it was the skirt which finally made the ACV practical, it is a good idea to examine the working of this helpful device at this point.

The development of flexible skirts not only made it possible for ACV's to gain greater clearance over waves and obstacles, it also brought increased efficiency to the hovercraft.

Even on small ACV's, the skirts are usually quite long. They hang from both the inner and outer edges of the peripheral air duct, as shown in Figure 5. The two skirts are held together in such a way that a "nozzle" is formed by them. Air from the lift fan enters *between* the two skirt walls, causing the space between skirts to inflate. The air is then discharged at the bottom of the skirts in the form of a jet. By doing this, the "daylight clearance" between the water or ground and the jets is generally about six inches—but the daylight clearance to the *metal or hard structure* of the craft is increased by the height of the skirts. Furthermore, the skirts are designed so that they will deflect easily upon hitting an object such as a wave, rock, or tree stump, with the result that the craft can pass over such projections without damage. In traversing obstacles, air cushion leakage is increased only momentarily as the skirts pass over the impeding object, but the cushion seal is promptly restored when the skirts drop back into normal position.

There are many types of flexible skirts as shown in Figure 6.

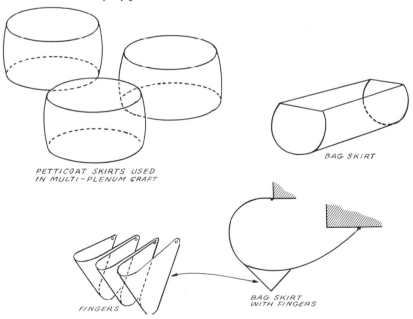

PETTICOAT SKIRTS USED
IN MULTI-PLENUM CRAFT

BAG SKIRT

FINGERS

BAG SKIRT
WITH FINGERS

Several types of flexible skirts

All of these skirts are flexible. They are usually constructed of a rubberized material, the most common being rubberized canvas, hypalm coated nylon fabric, neoprene.

Captured Air Bubble Ships

The second major class of SES consists of the *fixed wall craft*, which ride on "captured air bubbles," and hence their nickname "CAB's." In these craft, the *fixed* sidewalls, solid but slender, extend into the water like keels and block the escape of air from the

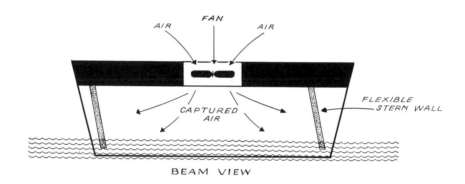

BEAM VIEW

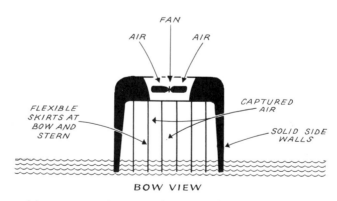

BOW VIEW

Bow and beam view of Captured Air Bubble Craft. (Also known in England as the "sidewall craft.")

chamber under deck. The bow and stern walls are flexible skirts. By increasing the pressure of the air which comprises the captured bubble—up to 60 pounds per square inch—the entire craft is lifted upwards, and the water drag is reduced, allowing the SES to go faster. Figure 7 is a view of a typical CAB.

In the CAB, the air bubble or cushion is trapped between the fixed sidewalls and the flexible seals at the bow and stern so that there is very little air leakage. As will be discussed in Chapter 10, it is this type of ship which will eventually result in large ocean-going craft, in excess of 10,000 tons, with the ship being powered either by gas turbine or a nuclear reactor (or perhaps a combination of the two) and propelled either by high speed propellers or water jets.

2

The Idea and the Invention

In one of the chilly basement rooms of the historic government buildings at Whitehall, in London, near the place where Henry the Eighth banqueted and Charles I was beheaded, one of the most revolutionary advances in the history of transport was about to be demonstrated in model form, in October, 1956. Crouched in the middle of the drafty, dusty room was the inventor, Mr. Christopher Sydney Cockerell, former electronics and radio engineer and part-time boat builder. Around the walls of the room stood three observers from the Ministry of Supply, obviously skeptical and impatient.

On his haunches, the bald-headed, mustached Mr. Cockerell held a string tied to his model, a tiny, crude device which represented several years of work, theory, trial and error, accomplishment and failure—and great promise—all based, however, on his cold-blooded and scientific development work. The 4½-ounce balsa model was an oval-shaped saucer, 33 inches in length, with a triangular tail and a hump-backed top. Inside the hump was a small "frog glow plug" gasoline motor, driving a propeller and sucking air through an intake on the rim of the saucer that resembled the open mouth of a frog. (See Figure 8.)

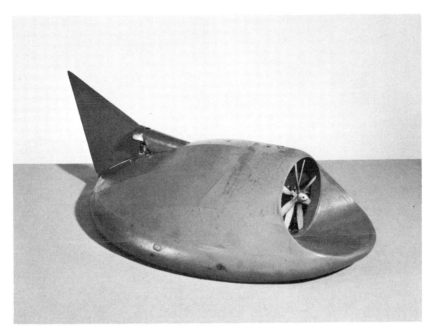

Top and underside views of Cockerell's first model

The room was filled with the stuttering noise of the engine as the saucer-shaped model commenced to move. Around and around the room, hauling its restraining string taut from a large weight in the middle of the floor, the small model whizzed past the legs of the observers, a little over a fraction of an inch above the floor, supported on its self-generated cushion of air.

At that noteworthy moment, the "hovercraft" had been born and demonstrated in miniature in England.

As is the case with most inventors, there was a restless, inquisitive spirit in Mr. Cockerell, which had alternately inspired and plagued him—and which finally changed his life. Trained and employed in electronics and radio engineering, aircraft radio and the beginnings of television for more than twenty years, Cockerell suddenly gave up his career in 1948 when his wife inherited some money.

The Cockerells sold their Chelmsford home and bought a trailer and boat hiring business at Somereyton, near Lowestoft, England, and soon they began designing and building boats jointly. The company was given the romantic name of "Ripplecraft." While Mr. Cockerell supervised the carpenters and craftsmen, Mrs. Cockerell worked on the interior fittings and sails.

As early as 1947, Mr. Cockerell, whose previous background had had nothing to do with the sea, had begun to look into the theory of boatbuilding. In this age of speed, why could boats not go faster? "Very soon, in reading about boats," he said, "I came upon the problem of wave resistance. This, of course, is a law of nature—that is, something that one cannot remove. All one can do (if other things permit) is to design so that it shall be a minimum."

In thinking about the problem, Mr. Cockerell decided that there were only two ways to move an object along a surface—it either rolls and tumbles, or it slides. Car and train wheels *roll*. Boats, skates and sleds *slide*.

It was the snow sleigh and the ice skates that eventually captured his attention. He knew that the steel runners of skates or a sled sliding across snow or ice create friction, melting a very thin layer of ice to form water, which serves as a lubricant. This allows the sleigh or ice skater to move rapidly, with much less friction.

How could he do the same for a boat sliding through water? Obviously, if he could get a lubricant between the boat's hull and the water's surface, he could reduce friction and increase speed. *Air* was the answer—the resistance of air is about 815 times less than that of water—but how could it be introduced and how could it be kept underneath the boat?

"One Sunday evening," Mr. Cockerell said, "I thought I would have a look at using an air curtain around the rim of the boat. First, I made a simple mathematical calculation about the power that would be needed, and the next day, on Sunday, I made an annular

Coffee Can Model. These two coffee cans, one inside the other, were used by Sir Christopher Cockerell to confirm his calculated predictions about lift. Air was blown by a hairdryer into the space between the two cans, which were suspended over a set of kitchen scales!

jet,* using two coffee cans. (See Figure 9.) I found that the air did indeed follow the "predicted" path and that there *was* a gain in lift. It was very exciting!"

Step by step, over four years, learning a little from each experiment, Mr. Cockerell began to see what would be required. "The evolution of my ideas between 1953-1957 was as follows," said Mr. Cockerell. "First, I made a 12 foot punt, by which I could measure resistance with and without air. Then I tried a sidewall craft with hinged doors at each end, and replaced the hinged doors by thin curtains of moving water. The next stage was the use of air curtains in place of water curtains. Flexible extensions to the hull with air curtains was the final stage."

On December 12, 1955, Mr. Cockerell applied for a British patent, and a year later he filed a patent application with the United States Patent Office, covering lift by means of peripheral annular jets.

Between 1953 and 1956, Mr. Cockerell had tried to "sell" his idea, but with scant success. He ran head on into the idea smashers. "It's not a ship," said the shipbuilders. "Go see the airplane builders." But the aircraft builders said, "It's not an aircraft. Try the shipbuilders." And the engine manufacturers said, "Sorry, it's not for us, but if you find someone who is interested, let us know."

"Progress was very slow," said Mr. Cockerell, "and my resources were stretched to the limit."

A neighboring boatbuilder, Mr. A. D. Truman, constructed the working balsa wood model which was tested first on the lawn, then on a nearby lake. It was the fall of 1956 that Cockerell received valuable encouragement from Mr. Ronald A. Shaw, who was then Assistant Director, Aircraft Research, in the Ministry of Supply of the United Kingdom.

After the demonstration in the basement room of the Ministry of Supply, the project was promptly classified as having military application. A small contract was placed with Saunders-Roe, Limited, an aircraft manufacturer, for verification. But, in general, the hover-

*An "annular" jet is a round curtain of air being blown out of the space between two circular surfaces.

craft project languished for almost two years.

Nevertheless, Mr. Cockerell continued his experiments on recirculation of air, and in 1957 he issued a report which concluded that a flexible skirt was a vital ingredient, if commercially successful hovercraft were ever to be practical.

In 1958, the project was declassified by the Ministry of Supply.

"I was now free," said Mr. Cockerell, "to take my project to the National Research Development Corporation. Here, I received timely and crucial help from Lord Halsbury, the Managing Director. In fact, he put it up to the NRDC Board and pushed it through by virtue of the chairman's casting vote. By such narrow margins do things get done!"

In October, 1958, therefore, it finally became possible for Saunders-Roe, led by a design team under the directorship, first of Mr. Brennan, and later of Mr. Richard Stanton-Jones, to begin construction of an actual experimental hovercraft. The team worked enthusiastically, putting in evening and weekend shifts. As will be recounted in the next chapter, it was this chain of events that led to the construction of the SR.N1 in only eight months time and its flight across the English Channel on July 25, 1959.

The ACV Idea in the USA*

Inventions always start as ideas, just as Cockerell's began. And, often, "inventions" are credited to people who not only have the idea, but who act promptly in reducing that idea to paper and filing a patent for it.

In the United States, there has been much debate about when and to whom the "invention" of hovercraft should be credited. The U.S. Patent Office in Washington, D.C. had the frustrating job of

---

*In this Chapter, I have traced only the modern history of ACV's which led to their development and use. However, American interest in the ACV principle dates back to 1876, when Mr. James B. Ward of San Francisco obtained a patent for an ACV machine. Another American pioneer was Mr. Douglas K. Warner of Florida who did considerable ACV research from 1928 until 1940. In England, Mr. James R. Porter was an important pioneer beginning in 1909, while A. V. Alcock of Australia did practical work as early as 1912. The name of Mr. T. J. Kaario of Finland who did pioneering work commencing in 1936 should also be mentioned.

Melville Beardsley in his "Fan-jet Skimmer," heading for the water

deciding this vexing question. The legal battle began with five claimants in what the U.S. Patent Office calls an "Interface Action." As stated previously, Mr. Cockerell filed his patent application in December, 1956. Four months later, a Lieutenant Colonel in the U.S. Air Force, Melville W. Beardsley, filed his application.

By 1964, the five contestants had been narrowed to two—Colonel Beardsley of the United States, and Mr. Cockerell of the United Kingdom.

After much wrangling and investigating, which lasted many months, Mr. Cockerell was adjudged the winner, because Colonel Beardsley was unable to produce sufficient evidence that he had applied "due diligence in reducing his invention to practice." The lawyers also decided that Mr. Cockerell had the earliest date for his patent application (that is, the theoretical idea), but they gave credit to Colonel Beardsley for the earliest date for "complete disclosure" (the practical application of the idea). A review of the record now shows that several other Americans besides Beardsley were engaged in building ACV's, or doing ACV research, and in some cases actually built and "flew" man-sized models before Mr. Cockerell.

Although Melville Beardsley lost the legal case, it is only fair to record the story of his original idea.

"I conceived the idea for the peripheral-jet ACV on 2 October, 1953, while I was a U.S. Air Force officer detailed to the University of Chicago, taking my masters in Research and Development Management. It was between semesters and it was 2 A.M. in the morning. I was alone, having just read a small item in the newspaper reporting a 'flying saucer.' I posed myself a problem: if there were flying saucers, and I was told to design one, how would I do it?

"Not being familiar with the control of gravity, I came out with a saucer-shaped body with a top center air inlet and a large centrifugal rotor blowing air down and underneath. It was obvious that the pressure would be greater if the peripheral jet were directed inwardly as well as downwardly. I *now* say it was obvious. It really wasn't at the time, but it did seem that pressure ought to be developed so that a vehicle could be lifted and moved over the ground or water without contact. I couldn't forget the idea. It kept bugging me.

"I tried many back-room small scale experiments with inconclusive results, and tried to generate interest in the possibilities of ACV's. You would be surprised at how many experts told me it wouldn't work. While all these skull sessions and experiments were going on, I was on active duty with the U.S. Air Force and burning a lot of midnight oil. It was a period of lots and lots of sweat and tears.

"Finally, two of my friends and I formed a corporation and in May, 1956, our company was awarded a contract to build an ACV. I resigned from active duty to devote my full attention to the task. We built the first ACV delivered to the Marine Corps and the Army; then a larger one for the Marines. (See Figure 11.)

Colonel Beardsley's first U.S. Marine Corps ACV

"At this point, in May, 1956, we were not aware of any British activity, although the record now shows that Mr. Cockerell was active before this.

"I then developed my Fan-Jet Skimmer in just two years. I felt then as I do now that small sport ACV's were going to have a great future, and it was a challenge to try to make a small vehicle that would attain hump speed on water carrying a 150 pound operator with one small engine. This effort was successful."

While Cockerell's and Beardsley's ideas and experiments were taking form, there were several other people in both Canada and the United States who contributed significantly to hovercraft development.

Franklin A. Dobson's first six-foot model

Franklin A. Dobson's first ACV being tested in a swimming pool.

One of these early pioneers in the United States was Mr. Franklin A. Dobson, who began his work in 1957.

"My work started as a by-product of a Vertical Take-Off design effort," he said. "I thought there should be some way to increase the ground effect of a helicopter by enclosing the rotor downwash, so I worked out the plenum chamber theory and later the annular jet. At the time, I wasn't aware of work being done elsewhere, either in the United States or Great Britain.

"To test my theory, I built a six-foot model with the help of a friend, using a homemade double rotor from an earlier VTOL experiment, plus a belt-drive from a chain saw engine. One whole weekend was devoted to the job, and the resulting vehicle, while hardly the ultimate in efficiency, checked the performance predictions quite closely." (See Figures 12 and 13.)

Mr. Dobson considers that one of his machines was among the first to surpass "hump speed," in 1963.

Another key person in the early idea period was Mr. Harvey R. Chaplin, a research engineer working at the U. S. Navy's David Taylor Model Basin, outside Washington, D.C. It was Chaplin who developed and published the first accurate mathematical description of the peripheral jet phenomenon, a solution which was to inspire others in the theory, and which would lead to actual hardware.

"I was completely fascinated," recalls Mr. Chaplin, "by what seemed to me the paradoxical result that one could get from a device providing a great deal more lift than the jet thrust supplied. I went to work with great enthusiasm to find a theoretical explanation. I succeeded in this and published my first paper on the subject, *Theory of the Annular Nozzle in Proximity to the Ground*, in July, 1957.

"I am proud of this report. It is one of the very few things I have ever written which I have not wished, within a few years, that I could change. At the time, and for a year or so afterward, I thought it was *the* original formulation of a valid annular jet theory. In reality, there were earlier valid theories developed in both the United Kingdom and Canada, as well as other U.S. researchers who were developing equivalent theories concurrently with mine. My report was, however, the first (and for some time the only) open publication of a valid theory, and I believe that it contributed significantly to the quality of U.S. research efforts which began to get underway in many laboratories and companies during the following two years."

Several other Americans were also pioneers. Mr. Tom Sweeney and Mr. Barney Nixon had been experimenting at Princeton University. This institution had entered the ACV research field rapidly in late 1958, under the "ALART" program of the U.S. Army's Aviation Laboratories at Fort Eustis, Virginia.

"At this time," recalls Mr. Nixon, "the British were stirring up considerable interest in the ACV concept, although several independent researchers in this country, including Tom Sweeney, had already been experimenting for some time. Our efforts were directed toward rather small amphibious and over-land type craft for the Army and concentrated mainly on stability, maneuverability, high speed aerodynamic effects, and the ground effect airplane concept."

Another unsung American pioneer of this early period was Mr. Walter A. Crowley, who commenced ACV work in 1956, filed his

Walter A. Crowley's 1956 model, one of the first man-carrying ACV's

first patent in 1958, and actually had a man-carrying model flying that same year—a nine-by-sixteen-foot machine—now on display at the National Air Museum, Smithsonian Institution, Washington, D.C. (See Figure 14.)

"I used two small drone aircraft engines," said Mr. Crowley, "one for thrust and steering and the other to blow air vertically below the machine to provide lift. This machine could carry three men about two inches off the ground or one man up to six inches."

Crowley demonstrated his model several times in 1958—at the Detroit arsenal, at Andrews Air Force Base, and at the Anacostia Naval Air Station.

Still another American pioneer was Dr. William R. Bertelsen, an Illinois physician and engineer, who became interested in air cushion craft in the early 1950's. "I entered the ground effect field because of an urgent need to improve transportation to and from rural patients," he said. "All-weather transportation in this age of space is still very poor, and there are many weeks of each year in the northern United States when roads are impassable."

Dr. Bertelsen therefore designed and built an aeromobile for reaching patients at farmhouses isolated by heavy snowfall—the first of thirteen different ACV machines he has since designed.

From a careful review of all the records, therefore, it appears that

Dr. William Bertelsen in his Aeromobile

quite a number of individuals, both in the United States and in Great Britain, were rediscovering the utility and application of air cushion vehicles between 1950-1956. It is certain, too, that in 1958 other men were farther ahead in actual development work involving man-carrying machines than was Cockerell. But when all the evidence is examined, it seems fair to give credit to Christopher Cockerell as the first inventor of a practical hovercraft, as the U.S. Patent Office has done. But it is also necessary and right to recognize the accomplishments and original work of such pioneers as Beardsley, Chaplin, Dobson, Bertelsen, Crowley, Nixon, and Sweeney, and their earlier predecessors like Ward and Warner in the United States, Alcock of Australia, Porter of England, and Kaario of Finland.

For his invention, Mr. Cockerell was made a Knight Bachelor by Queen Elizabeth in 1969.

3

Calais to Dover—
The First Hovercraft
Crossing of the English
Channel, July 25, 1959

Getting Ready

One of the memorable and historic dates for hovercraft, second only in importance to October, 1956, when Sir Christopher did his model demonstration for the Admiralty and Ministry of Supply observers, is July 25, 1959, for it was on this day, at 4:55 A.M., on a Saturday morning, that the experimental SR.N1 set off from the flat calm of Calais harbor in France to Dover, England. This was the first hovercraft crossing of an open body of water—the choppy and legendary English Channel—a twenty-five mile journey that was to give birth to a new industry and transportation system. The flight of the SR.N1, a crude noisy, ugly machine, would ignite an intensive development program which in only ten years would produce a new category of military machines, a new sporting craze, and give impetus to a shipbuilding revolution.

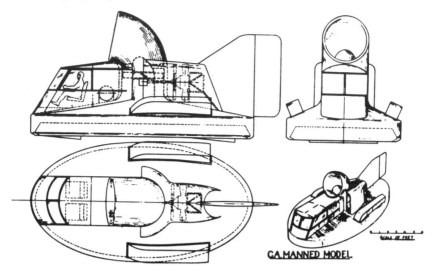

CA.MANNED MODEL

The original SR-N1 proposal

Building the SR.N1

Let us begin the story a year earlier, in September of 1958, and with the two persons who designed the history-making SR.N1—Mr. Brennan and Mr. Richard Stanton-Jones, the Chief Designer of Saunders-Roe, Limited.

"The SR.N1 started life about the middle of 1958," Stanton-Jones recalls, "but in those days it looked rather different from the machine which first crossed the Channel." (See Figure 16.)

Stanton-Jones' first design, in fact, called for the experimental model to weigh only 4,000 pounds, have an airspeed of 30 knots, and a hover height of one or two feet. The final machine was to be quite different.

Detailed planning for the craft was begun in October of the same year.

"It soon became clear," said Mr. Stanton-Jones, "that our first thoughts would need considerable modification." The plenum chamber design was not efficient, and severe air losses could be foreseen, so Stanton-Jones and his team developed a more conventional ducting arrangement. In only one month, the original design sketch had begun to take on a quite different appearance. (See Figure 17.)

So confident of eventual success was the team that a simultaneous building program was undertaken, along with the design work itself. Stability and control were among the first problems. So was propulsion. Would a single jet power plant provide both stability and power? In the interest of economy, Stanton-Jones decided against a separate engine for a stern propeller (which would have permitted reverse thrust for a fast slowdown). Instead, after proving the craft's potential stability with one-third full-scale model, Stanton-Jones chose a twin jet power system. All these modifications meant the SR.N1 was growing—up already from 4,000 to 6,600 pounds.

Meanwhile, the actual construction was proceeding, and modifications were incorporated as experiments were tried and ideas tested.

Many of the problems were practical ones—if the SR.N1, for example, was to cross a choppy English Channel, it obviously would encounter waves, and even the small ones could be a problem. And what if the SR.N1 nosed into a wave? Or what if it crashed into a half-submerged log? Hull strength and support had to be built in—and the operators and riders had to have some place to sit while they drove and rode. The engine had to be mounted, so it could be worked on easily and effectively.

SR-N1, the first hovercraft to cross the English Channel, on July 25, 1959

By now, the original design weight had more than doubled—up to 8,500 pounds—and, naturally, the more the weight, the greater the power required, and the less the hover height.

But despite all the problems and worries, Stanton-Jones pushed his team on. Finally, the SR.N1 was completed in only eight months, two months ahead of schedule.

"During the early trials of the craft," the designer said, "we ran into the usual crop of development problems. The engine cooling was not right, the control valves fluttered, and worst of all, our original design for the propulsion duct control was almost completely unmanageable. The system had to be completely revised."

There were other lessons and problems—dust and dirt on land, and spray and salt on the sea.

"During a two-hour operation," continued Stanton-Jones, "we got as much as a quarter-of-an-inch of salt on the cylinders of our engine, and after each operation we had to wash down the whole machine completely with fresh water."

The Crossing

After the initial tests, which took place in the Solent, near Southampton, England, and which proved that the new craft worked and could make about 22 knots in calm air, the Saunders-Roe design and construction teams were ready to undertake a public experiment—one which would capture headlines and create interest and perhaps even business. Crossing the English Channel came to mind immediately, and so did the date—July 25, 1959—the fiftieth anniversary of the first airplane flight across the Channel by Bleriot.

When this publicity scheme was presented to the Directors of Saunders-Roe, however, there was little enthusiasm. What would a failure do to the company? Might it not doom the whole project? After a few weeks of discussion and debate, however, the Directors accepted the idea and gave the go-ahead.

For an account of the world's first public hovercraft flight, let the inventor himself, Sir Christopher S. Cockerell, tell the story in his own inimitable style:

Sir Christopher Cockerell

"Our plan was to go from Dover to Calais; but the weather fore-cast for that week in July was east or northeast winds for some days —*headwinds*. So, after thinking things over, we decided that it would be more complimentary to the French if we reversed our plan and tackled the crossing from Calais to Dover."

With the SR.N1 capable of only 22 knots, a 10-knot headwind would make the actual ground speed only 12 knots. Better to have a tailwind!

Sir Christopher also remembered how Bleriot, the Frenchman, had stolen a march on his English competitor, who had planned to take off before him that morning fifty years earlier and become a hero. But on arising, the now-forgotten Englishman decided that flying conditions were not right and went back to bed—and thus lost the race.

"Bleriot set off," said Sir Christopher, "and some 25 minutes later in mid-Channel, his engine began to overheat. Twenty-five minutes was as long as he had ever managed to keep it running. Luckily, a heavy rain storm started, cooled his 25 horsepower engine, and it regained its power. He landed in a little field on the Dover Cliffs."

The lessons to be learned from this problem-ridden flight obviously were, first, not to be overly discouraged by Channel weather in July at 5 o'clock in the morning and, second, to push on confidently past the obstacles.

The first obstacle was British customs. "Did Saunders-Roe, Cockerell, or Stanton-Jones," the custom official asked, "have an export license to take that odd-looking contraption—what do you call it, a *hovercraft?*—out of England?"

"Much ink!" remembers Cockerell. So a license was gotten.

And how were they to get "The Flying Saucer" across to Calais, so it could fly back again?

Her Majesty's Navy had the answer—and agreed to provide a tug and a self-propelled barge, called a "flatty." *HMS Warden* was the tug's name.

Thus, the SR.N1 made her first trip across the Channel on Friday, July 24, sitting on a barge escorted by *Warden.* It was a bad day. The wind was strong and the waves four feet high, with whitecaps everywhere. Cockerell, Stanton-Jones, and the Chief Test Pilot, LCDR Peter Lamb, were disconsolate.

"What to do?" questioned Sir Christopher. "Too much wind and sea to attempt the crossing, so we went out in the naval tug and wallowed about in mid-Channel and observed the sea, and rather ran out of conversation and felt depressed.

"We returned to Calais about 4 P.M., and found rather large crowds, all expecting us to do something, so we decided to give a demonstration. While the British Navy had cleared the trip with the French Ministry of Marine, nobody had notified the French Ministry of Aviation. These officials now appeared. Was it an aeroplane or was it a ship? There do not seem to be any Hovercraft forms yet. Long, extremely polite arguments—maybe it was a ship. Exit polite official.*

"The SR.N1 was cast off, and Peter Lamb, our pilot, scooted her about the harbor," continued Sir Christopher, "then went out of the harbor and turned for the flat sandy beach. It was swarming with people. We came in slowly, and the people divided in front of us and closed up behind us, but the craft seemed to want to go its own way—in fact, it was making for a very pretty girl in a bikini. However, she fled, and Peter Lamb managed to turn the craft round. We went out to sea again and came back in over the sands again—and, of course, there was the girl in the bikini! So it looks as if Hovercraft are not She-like ships—but it could, of course, have been *pilot* trouble!"

Peter Lamb's gaze, however, was not on the bikini, but on an insane spectator who was lying down in front of the SR.N1 to ascertain whether or not it had wheels!

After the nonscheduled demonstration, the team settled down for the night in *Warden's* tiny sick bay. There was little sleep, only anxiety and worry. Would the weather be any better in the morning?

"The following morning at 3:30 A.M.," remembers Peter Lamb, "there was a flat calm, and after a brief look at the sea outside the harbor, I decided to make the attempt with as little delay as possible. The ground crew, with commendable foresight, had hoisted the craft off the lighter, warmed up the engine, and topped up the fuel tanks. As a safety precaution, in view of the lack of following wind, I also decided to take aboard sixteen additional gallons in cans on the deck of the SR.N1."

No time for breakfast. Cockerell, Stanton-Jones, and Lamb had a final look at the weather outside the harbor in the still dark morning. It was a near perfect day—a light wind, a little mist, and a gentle

*This question—was the hovercraft an aeroplane or a ship?—would one day be debated in the House of Lords, and discussed by the International Civil Aeronautical Organization (ICAO). (See Chapter 9.)

swell. The decision was confirmed—Go!

Stanton-Jones debarked and got in the accompanying RAF launch, which would escort the hovercraft, while Mr. J. B. Chaplin got aboard. Chaplin and Cockerell would serve as "moveable ballast."*

And so, the memorable trip commenced from Calais harbor—Peter Lamb steering 294° True with 2700 RPM on the engine. The distance to Dover was twenty-five nautical miles. The loom of the South Foreland light near Dover was *still* faintly visible in the early morning light.

Gathering momentum, the SR.N1 achieved hump speed, reaching 22 knots from time to time. The RAF rescue launch buzzed alongside and provided navigation. About 5:30 A.M., the white cliffs of Dover, tinged red in the morning sunrise, began to be visible.

"There was a light wind from the northeast," recalled Sir Christopher, "and the swell was mostly on our aft quarter, but occasionally one was with us, and it was exhilarating to skim down the face of it and rush up the next. The fine salt spray kicked up by the jets got into everything and made one's eyes stream. So, for a time I didn't look—and then when I did, there, faintly, were the Cliffs of Dover! How many people in history have been gladdened by that sight!"

By now, the SR.N1 had reached mid-Channel, where the wind increased, causing some minor troubles for Lamb.

But a major headache was just appearing—a small boat to port whose course and nearness made a collision almost certain!

"Although I had the right-of-way," said Lamb, "it was apparent he wasn't keeping a good lookout, so I altered course to starboard, and slowed down, settling onto the water."

After this near collision, because of the wind and swell, now four feet high, it took Lamb quite some time to get the SR.N1 above "hump speed" again. From the RAF rescue launch, Stanton-Jones

---

*Sir Christopher later wrote the author that "Chaplin actually traveled in the cockpit and I was left sitting on the bow, getting sopping wet."

watched the SR.N1 digging its nose into one wave after another.

"It once disappeared into the troughs," he said, "so that only the portion above the propulsion ducts was visible."

Still the SR.N1 pressed on.

"I was sopping wet and rather cold," said Sir Christopher, "but the cliffs really were larger now, about two miles off.

"Soon we were under the cliffs, shielded from the wind, with a flat sea. I observed the wash. At hump speed, the SR.N1 trails about 18-inch waves but at this speed, about 25 or 30 knots, there is absolutely no wave formation to be seen, just water stroked by a shaving brush.

"Into Dover harbor we came, across it at almost 30 knots—and there was the beach, a very steep shingle beach. Up we went and came to rest—and I fell off aft, due to the angle, along with a couple of empty petrol cans. It was 6:58 A.M., and it was over. Breakfast—that is what I wanted most."

The first personnel to board the craft were the ubiquitous British custom officials.

"Anything to declare?" they asked.

Peter Lamb, the chief pilot, replied for everyone, "No, but it's good to be in England."

"That appeared to satisfy one and all," Lamb said.

The world's first hovercraft journey across a well-known body of water was over, proving it could be done. But it was a crude and chancey beginning.

"We were lucky to get away with it," concluded Sir Christopher.

4

Monsters in Combat

After the initial success of the SR.N1, military interest in the potential of ACV's began to appear in many countries—but the first employment of ACV's in combat fell to the United States Navy, in Vietnam in 1966.

In July, 1965, three commercial SRN5's were purchased by the Navy from Bell Aerosystems Company and modified for military service, including machine guns and armor plate.

In September of the same year, a crew of forty officers and sailors commenced ACV training in Buffalo, on Lake Erie. It was here that a sailor converted the PACV initials into the spoken term, "PAK-V"—a term which has since stuck in nautical lingo. And it was here, too, that the crew (to become Coastal Division 17 later) met their new Commanding Officer, Lieutenant Kenneth H. Luenser. An ex-white hat, Luenser had a total of nine years in the Navy, including "tin can" (destroyer) and "alligator" (amphibious) service. It would be Luenser's honor and responsibility to train the crews and take the three PAK-V's into combat.

Lieutenant Luenser started his sailors' program with some rough-water operations in the surf off Coronado, California, and Tijuana, Mexico. Gun crews fired the 50 caliber guns mounted on the hovercraft for proficiency, and the mechanics learned how to handle the T-58 engine and make skirt repairs.

"The most difficult part of the pilot training," said Lieutenant Luenser, "was a high speed turn at night on the open ocean. With no visible reference points as an aid, it was quite difficult to tell how much side slip there was, and if the PAK-V was actually moving in the direction the bow was moving—or whether the PAK-V was moving sideways."

Luenser recalls, "With our three PAK-V's parked on the ship's well deck, we left for Vietnam on the 17th of March, 1966, aboard USS *Cabildo* (LSD-16) and arrived at Cat Lo, about twenty-five miles southeast of Saigon, on the 2nd of May. Our first operations were patrol missions surveilling the coast, using USS *Tortuga* (LSD-26) as our operating base." *Tortuga* was anchored eleven miles off the muddy Mekong Delta, between the Co Chien and Bassac Rivers.

"Most of our patrols were at night," said Luenser, "and we quickly discovered that the loud noise of our engines made all the Viet Cong sampans run for cover. So we learned to land the PAK-V on a mud flat, stop the engine and listen—or else we'd just drift in the river. With our binoculars and radar, we'd look for infiltrators. When we saw a junk or sampan, we'd light off the jet. dash up and catch them, and board and search." (See Figure 19.)

Lieutenant Luenser and his crew soon contrived a simple thumb rule for telling the difference between a sampan and a junk. "We used the Vietnamese definition," he said. "If you could load a water buffalo athwartships, it was a junk. Anything smaller was a sampan."

The first month of operations proved that the PAK-V's needed some modifications—more guns, both in the topside turret and at the side windows, a spray shield for the gunner, lights for the cabin, a table for the navigator's chart, and, most important of all, a platform around the hull on which the crewmen could walk and work.

But confidence in the combat capability of the Monsters was growing. "In combat operations we felt quite secure in the

PAK-V," said Lieutenant Luenser, "not secure in the sense that we were protected from gunfire because there *was* no protection other than the PAK-V's speed. But we felt secure in that as long as we could keep the engine running, the PAK-V would get us back to our base. On two occasions, large tears occurred in the skirt, and on two other occasions, large holes, approximately 3' x 5' were made in the plenum chamber. On all four occasions, the PAK-V made it back under its own steam, once passing through a four-foot surf to do so. Twice in the Plain of Reeds we had to effect temporary repairs. Because of the simple design of the craft, this was done quite easily. On another occasion, the steering cable parted. We rigged lines to the rudder on the outside of the craft and stationed men outside with phone communications to the pilot. When he wanted to turn to the left, he told the men to heave around. Another thrilling moment during a combat mission occurred when the rudder post broke. Since it is made of aluminum tubing, we repaired it with a broom handle and an empty beer can!"

The next mission for the PAK-V's was to be tougher—patrols in the rivers of the Delta itself. Operating from Cat Lo, their task would be to enforce curfews and stop the Viet Cong infiltration of men and supplies. This was Cong country of the toughest type— where pirates, smugglers, and bandits had operated for centuries— rough, determined men who knew the swamps and mud of the Delta better than the fish themselves.

To understand the task of trying to control the Mekong Delta, the reader must understand something of its geography. (See Figure 20.) The whole area is low and subject to prolonged flooding. Perhaps half of it is rice paddy, marsh, and swamp land. Two principal rivers cross it—the Mekong and the Bassac—with the Mekong having three main outlets to the sea. The entire Delta is a lacework of unnumbered streams and canals, totalling 3,000 miles of waterways for small boats. In the heavy rains of the Southwest monsoon season, May to October, the water can rise as much as three to five feet.

About fifty per cent of the population of South Vietnam lives in the Delta, the majority of them along the rivers and canals. Also

Above: U.S. Navy PAK-V alongside a Vietnamese sampan. Below: PAK-V in action in the Mekong Delta

along these waterways are numerous four-foot-high embankments, many of which are tree lined—ideal locations for ambush sites and hideaways.

And in this area are thousands upon thousands of small sampans of every variety.

To stop the "bad" guys from using this network was the Navy's job, and the PAK-V's were to join the operation nicknamed "Game Warden."

"I must admit we had some worries about how well our Monsters could take enemy gunfire," recalls Lieutenant Luenser. "We knew our PAK-V's were tender, thin-skinned, and noisy—but we had two advantages: speed and firepower."

For the next six months, the Monsters cruised up and down the roiling, muddy waters of the Mekong and its lacelike tributaries, giving better than they got—and not once getting hit.

"The VC would be along the riverbanks and wait for the PAK-V's to pass by," said Lieutenant (junior grade) Thomas M. Graves, the Division's Supply Officer. "Then they'd open up with 200-300 rounds. But our crews reacted so quickly that we were able to suppress the firing in every case. Also, I think our speed had a lot to do with our not getting hit."

For a "craft" that had been invented only seven years earlier, the Monsters were learning fast.

The Plain of Reeds

The most effective use of the PAK-V's in 1966 took place in that large area west of Saigon known as the "Plain of Reeds." (See Figure 20.) Like most areas of the Delta, the Plain of Reeds is flat, often flooded by water, and covered with a dense growth of heavy swamp grass, reeds, and bramble-type bushes three to ten feet high. Adjacent to the thousands of waterways are many wooded areas, saplings four inches thick and ten feet high. In addition to those four-foot embankments mentioned earlier, dikes line the waterways, providing ideal hiding places for guerrillas.

Of all the areas of the vast Mekong Delta, the Viet Cong enemy

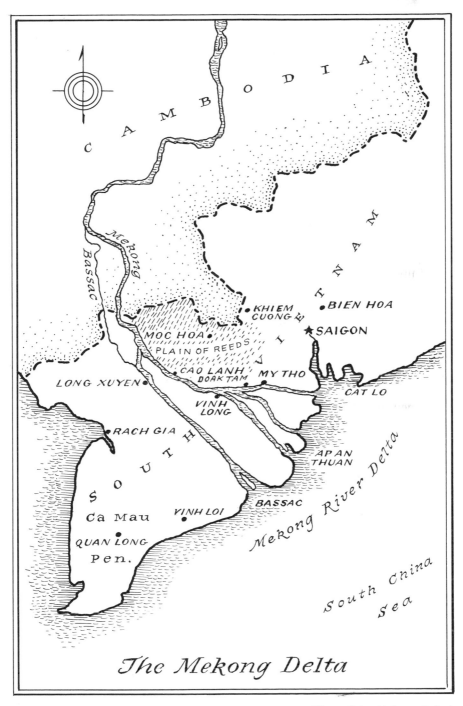

(Map of the Mekong Delta)

U.S. Navy PAK-V operating near a village

enjoyed greater freedom in the Plain of Reeds than anywhere else, and it was here that they exerted almost total control. Their base camps consisted of hutches, caches, and bunkers, widely dispersed and well concealed in the heavy grass, embankments, trees, and vegetation. In many areas were hidden small arms factories, making guns, grenades and mines. The only positive means of finding the enemy in such a tangled area was to go in and hunt—foot by foot and village by village. Even low flying helicopters often could not see the igloo type bunkers hidden beneath the grass and trees—igloos made of baked clay and grass, two to four feet thick and framed with logs. A "search and clear" by foot soldiers in this area of few roads and poor maps was a herculean task.

But if the Plain of Reeds was ideal territory for the elusive Viet Cong, it was also ideal for the fast moving, highly mobile PAK-V's.

The Plain of Reeds' operation took place from November 20 through December 5, 1966, and received the code name "Operation Quai Vat" which, liberally translated from the Vietnamese language, means "The Monster."

To carry out this theme, the crews of the three PAK-V's painted the bows of their round-nosed craft like grinning monsters, their mouths filled with shark's teeth.

On November 20 the three PAK-V's moved from Cat Lo to their new temporary base of Moc Hoa, a district village of several thousand population. Moc Hoa was only four miles from Cambodia and very near the hidden Viet Cong guerrilla sanctuaries across the border.

"The only real estate near Moc Hoa under control of South Vietnam," said Lieutenant Luenser, "was in the immediate vicinity of Moc Hoa and the base camps. The countryside itself was all Cong country. Every canal and tree line had bunkers and fortifications which, in late November, were drying out from the monsoon floods and we knew that Charlie was moving back in."

For this operation, each of the three PAK-V's would carry one officer and four men, plus a dozen Special Force troops, who would ride outside. The PAK-V's were led by four officers who rotated among the three craft: Lieutenant Roy E. Adair, Jr., Lieutenant

Shark's Teeth on PAK-V

Michael Vincent, Lieutenant (junior grade) Kipston Kumler, and Lieutenant (junior grade) Frank B. W. McCollum. Usually, the three PAK-V's would stay together during these search and clear missions and be supported by one or more helicopters. What the PAK-V's could not see through the thick, twelve-foot grass, the helicopters could see from above—and what the helicopters could not see amidst the dense tree growths, the PAK-V's could—so it was an ideal combination.

Each mission started by selecting a suspect Cong area near to Moc Hoa, using both friendly reports and photographs. The PAK-V's and helos would move into the search area at high speed, debarking the troops in suspected areas to search huts, bunkers and tree groves.

Lieutenant McCollum described a typical mission:

"Following a report from the helicopter pilot that he had spotted a camouflaged sampan," he said, "we moved into the area, but the vegetation was so dense that it took us three or four passes before we located the sampan—it looked like it had just been abandoned, for our South Vietnamese troops found hand grenades, posters and medical supplies in the sampan. It wasn't long after that they captured one Viet Cong who was trying to hide nearby under the water by breathing through a reed."

Sampans proved particularly easy prey for the rampaging, fast moving PAK-V's. "We found that the best way to destroy a sampan," said Lieutenant Roy Adair, "was simply to run over it."

It did not take long before it became evident that, by using both PAK-V's and helos, plus good intelligence, the Viet Cong could be trapped in their lairs.

For two weeks, the PAK-V's swept the Plain of Reeds. When all the missions had been added up, they had been credited with 23 Viet Cong killed in action, the destruction of 71 sampans, 71 hutches, and enemy igloos, and the capture of much ammunition and supplies.

"Operation Monster" was a small beginning by American forces in the Mekong Delta—a beginning which would lead to increasing involvement throughout the Delta area in 1968-1969. Denying the Delta to the Viet Cong brought the hope of freedom to that long imprisoned area.

The Second U.S. Navy PAK-V Deployment

As a result of the initial Mekong Delta experience, the Navy decided to deploy the PAK-V's a second time, but before doing so, to bring them back to the United States for modification and reconditioning. This took place from February to July, 1967.

Many changes had to be made. The old skirts were replaced by the new "finger" skirts, which improved the maintenance, since individual "fingers" could be easily replaced. Moreover, the new skirt permitted the PAK-V's to operate with less "daylight clearance" (air gap) and hence less power and less spray.

Two extra fuel tanks were also added. The center window of the front door was modified to open inwards, both to provide ventilation and to permit the firing forward of a 50 caliber gun. The single 50 caliber turret was changed to accept twin 50's.

As a result of these modifications, the PAK-V's empty weight increased from 10,600 pounds to 11,500 pounds—but the new engine, with its greater power, still gave a maximum speed of 52 knots.

The PAK-V's returned to the Plain of Reeds on December 4, 1967. Here they continued operations until June 27, 1968, when they were moved north to Tan My, near Hue, in the northern part of South Vietnam.

A new commanding officer, Lieutenant Lloyd G. McIntyre, relieved Lieutenant Luenser on August 31, and the PAK-V's also received a new title—Coastal Division 17.

The Tan My area was another excellent one for the PAK-V's— over 200 square kilometers of waterways and more than 300 square kilometers of lowland and rice paddy—and the trio of PAK-V's saw a threefold increase in operations. The main operating area would be the Dam Cau Hai, a large bay which was too shallow in the dry season for anything except the PAK-V's to navigate. In this area, where hundreds of sampans were common, a curfew was in effect between 6 P.M., and 6 A.M. Anything that moved during darkness was presumed to be hostile.

A typical and one of the biggest PAK-V operations came on August 9, 1968, when a joint Army-Navy-Marine action, supported by the Monsters, took place four miles from Hue. The plan called for the infantrymen of the 101st Cavalry Division to approach two villages, Trieu Son and An Truyen, by boat and, on purpose, let the enemy escape toward the coast. The PAK-V's would then move in from behind, across the mud flats, and seal off all escape routes.

"It was our mission," said Lieutenant McIntyre, "to herd the escaping fishing craft back toward the shoreline, where Army troops would search them and check their papers."

Lieutenant Colonel Jim I. Hunt, Commander of the First Battalion, 501st Infantry, described how the day's operation was set in motion and its development.

Lieutenant Colonel Jim I. Hunt, U.S. Army, on an operation near Tan My, South Vietnam

"Our intelligence indicated that there was normally a platoon of Viet Cong in the two villages near the water," he said, "and their normal reaction whenever our troops started moving in was for the Viet Cong to head out into the water in sampans and spend the day hiding in their boats in the shallow water.

"So we decided to cordon off the area with two companies of my battalion, move inland and deliberately let the enemy see us, just like a normal ground operation. We deliberately kept all aircraft and helicopters out of the air, so as not to force the Viet Cong underground, but to let them get on out into the water.

"I allowed sufficient time for the enemy troops to do this, before ordering the PAK-V's into action. They moved in as my troops closed the trap and herded the sampans into the collection point."

Lieutenant McIntyre used two of his three PAK-V's for the mission.

"The Viet Cong had gotten pretty used to the normal type of land operation," said Lieutenant McIntyre. "Whenever our troops came into the villages, the enemy would fire a couple of warning shots and all the Charlies would take off in the opposite direction, jumping into the bay and hiding under the fishing weirs and breathing through reeds until our troops left. The ones who had sampans used them to escape. On the other hand, if our side used helicopters, the enemy troops would hide in any of the numerous bunkers in the hamlets."

Lieutenant Colonel Hunt's two companies approached the villages as before, the two warning shots were fired, and the enemy troops headed for the bay and their boats. There was a silent scramble to move away in the sampans.

"After they got out into the bay," said Lieutenant McIntyre, "we lit off our engines and went roaring down on them. They were caught by surprise, because in the past, the regular patrol boats hadn't been able to get through the shallow water."

The sampans were quickly surrounded and herded into an area. Individual Viet Cong, some hiding under overturned sampans, and others hidden alongside the fishing weirs, were quickly brought to the surface by a few concussion grenades.

When all the enemy were counted, the results were forty-two enemy killed in action and ninety-eight captured—without a single friendly casualty.

"After the operation was over," said Lieutenant McIntyre, "some of the people who had been unfriendly came over to our side willingly. They told us that their prime reason for defecting was that they were afraid of the Monsters because they felt they couldn't escape from them."

5

The New Cavalry—
The Army ACV's

As the Navy's combat experience from two deployments mounted, the U.S. Army's interest intensified. The Army also believed the ACV's had unique military capabilities, particularly in terrain like Vietnam. But the Army wanted certain improvements in its machines—such as more cabin space and a bigger front door (so a jeep could be loaded). Also, it was decided that the side air intakes should be eliminated and thereby decrease the ingestion of dust and salt spray into the engine. Flat outer decks should also be added, and a larger engine (1150 HP) was needed.

Thus the U.S. Army's ACV's were the first to be built from the keel up as combat vehicles and the first to be wholly built in the United States—in contrast to the Navy's conversion of British-built commercial models. The Army purchased three Bell SK-5's (see Figure 24) and tagged the first two as AACV's (Assault Air Cushion Vehicles). The third was given the initials TACV (Transport Air Cushion Vehicle).

The AACV crew consisted of a "driver" or operator (not "pilot"), two gunners who manned the 50 calibers in the roof turrets,

The First U.S. Army ACV's. In the foreground are two assault air cushion vehicles and in the background are two commercial ones. On a four-foot-thick cushion of air, they ride over land, water, mud flats, marsh or rice paddies.

two 7.62 gunners, one radar operator and one gunner for the M-5 grenade launcher—a total of seven. TACV was similarly manned.

From February to April, 1968, the Army trained its crews at the Aberdeen Proving Grounds, Maryland. The new "finger" skirts (see Figure 6, Chapter 1) reduced spray considerably. A new radar permitted the three craft to operate together as a single unit, and the new puff ports* gave much better stability and control. These machines were obviously superior to the old ones for the tasks of the Delta.

The Army ACV's arrived at Dong Tam on the 10th of May, 1968.

The U.S. Army's first ACV combat commander was Major David G. Moore, a veteran twenty-nine-year-old armor officer. As Commanding Officer of the ACV unit, attached to the Ninth Infantry Division, it would be his job to put the three vehicles into service.

"We were delighted with the ACV's from the very beginning," he reported. "We found out that, with the new puff ports, and increased power, they were easier to drive than a chopper but harder to drive than a tank."

According to Major Moore, the ACV has four advantages. "The first is that it has an all-weather, day or night capability," Moore said. "We can take winds of up to 25 knots and can still maneuver in greater gusts, with a little difficulty. Also, our radar made it possible to travel in the worst weather."

*Puff ports are small, horizontal air ducts built into the side of an ACV which aid in controlling the vehicle. They are used primarily at speeds up to 15 knots, and operate much like spacecraft thrusters. When air is allowed to escape through them, the ACV is pushed in the opposite direction. At speeds above 15 knots, the tail rudders begin to take effect.

Major David C. Moore, a veteran twenty-nine-year-old armor officer, is shown in the driver's seat of an ACV in action in Vietnam

The high-speed ACV's deployed by the U.S. Army in South Vietnam are armed and armored. The antenna aft is part of the radar navigation system.

"The second asset is the craft's ability to remain on station for long periods," Moore decided.

"The third advantage is the augmented firepower," Moore reported. "With our fuel capacity, we could stay out for up to six hours at one time . . . also, we could carry more firepower and ammo than helicopters—in fact, three times more firepower than a Huey Cobra.

"Lastly, ACV's were actually on the ground, occupying and holding a piece of it. Helicopters are fine for solid ground and boats are fine in water. But ACV's can work on both these surfaces, plus that swampy muck that neither of the craft can use."

Moore said the major job of his unit was to develop new tactics which would make optimum use of ACV speed and firepower. "We were used both for assault and reconnaissance. Our primary missions were reconnaissance in force and offensive missions."

The Army ACV's saw combat on June 7, 1968. All three roared off on a five-hour search and clear mission, each carrying ten U.S. troops.

"On our first trip," said Major Moore, "we went where it was possible to deliver troops that couldn't have gotten there any other way."

From June through November, 1968, the ACV's operated in the Mekong Delta, 40 combat missions in all—20 offensive missions, 11 search and clear operations, 5 raids, and 4 reconnaissance in force. In addition, there were 8 security missions and 11 logistic or service missions—for a grand total of 59.

The search and clear operation, as the name implies, was a methodical search of an assigned area, whereas a reconnaissance in force was designed to make contact with large enemy units.

Throughout this period, Major Moore operated his ACV's in all kinds of weather—winds up to 40 knots, heavy rainstorms, temperatures as high as 95°, and across the worst terrain the Delta could offer.

"Our reconnaissance in force mission on 14 October was typical of our work," continued Major Moore. "Using two of the

Muck and marsh are no obstacles for this amphibious Air Cushion Vehicle in action in the Mekong Delta.

three ACV's, with 24 U.S. soldiers aboard, we spent a whole day covering the area east of Dong Tam, approximately thirty miles south of Saigon. We also had scout helicopters helping us spot targets.

"One of these scout helicopters, while making a low-level reconnaissance run, was fired on by enemy automatic weapons. The helo pilot marked the target area and the ACV's closed the target area, broke through the island brush and overran the enemy position. Each ACV carried an infantry squad which dismounted to make a more thorough search.

"We made multiple insertions of the troops," reported Moore. "We searched the hootches and hutches we found, and we chased Vietcong across the rice paddies. In that one day, we killed 22 Charlies, took 20 prisoners, captured 400 pounds of weapons, packs and documents, and had not a single one of our men wounded or killed. It really showed that in this type of terrain, and using helicopters as back-up, you could do the job."

When the records were compiled, the ACV's had accounted for 48 killed in action and 107 prisoners at the cost of one American killed in action and four wounded.

It was beginning to look like the U.S. Army had at long last found the replacement for the horse cavalry—the ACV's.

6

Commuter and Ferryboat
Hovercraft

No invention in modern history has progressed so rapidly as the hovercraft. Its impact on the field of maritime transport, ferry operations, commuter service, exploration, cargo hauling, and recreation started only three years after that initial English Channel crossing in 1959. During the first decade, many commercial services were instituted—English Channel, Irish Sea, Bahamas, Kingston, Puget Sound, Cote D'Azur, Sydney Harbor, to name but a few. By 1968, a 160-ton Mountbatten Class SR.N4, the *Princess Margaret*, had commenced hauling cars and passengers between Dover and Boulogne. (See Figure 25.) In 1969, her cross-channel service was doubled. She can transport 254 passengers and 30 automobiles at a mile-a-minute speed.

The year 1962 saw the summertime introduction in England of the first hovercraft services for fare-paying passengers. The route was across the mouth of the River Dee, between Wales and Cheshire. Shortly thereafter, a commercial service by one 52-passenger SR.N2 started between Southsea and Ryde, Isle of Wight. The hovercraft reduced the normal ferry time from thirty minutes to approximately eight minutes.

The SR-N4, Mountbatten Class, *Princess Margaret,* the first commercial ACV in service across the English Channel.

The Vosper VT-1, latest example of a new breed of speedy ACV's for use on rivers and lakes, also for channel crossings and large city commuter services.

During the 1967-8 Expo World's Fair in Montreal, two SR.N6's carried 366,633 passengers up and down the St. Lawrence River.

Why has travel by hovercraft attained such instant and ever-increasing popularity?

First of all, it is fast—the average ferry trips can be cut by at least half the time. Secondly, it is safe. The traveler who fears an overwater airplane flight has learned that hovercraft "fly" only inches above the waves. Moreover, the big hovercraft "saucers" are inherently stable. In the unlikely event of complete engine failure, the hovercraft is equipped with anchors, distress signals and radio equivalent to ship standards. The hovercraft itself, with great reserves of built-in buoyancy, is hardly sinkable.

Third, the hovercraft is a new and novel way to travel—one can "write home about it"—as thousands have done, for example, during the Expo World's Fair at Montreal. (See Figure 26.)

Fourth, the hovercraft has offered, in many instances, the only available way to travel, for it provides a means of reliable transportation in roadless countries—by river, on across shoal water, sand bars, rapids, and rocks, through which no other waterborne vessel can transit. There are numerous undeveloped countries in Africa and South America which hovercraft can "open" by making the rivers their first highways.

Fifth, in the crowded cities of the world (nearly all of which are located on open water or on rivers), the hovercraft gives promise of relieving the inner city traffic jams caused by the automobile. For the millions living in suburban areas who commute daily into big cities, the hovercraft offers a fast and new way to transfer from home to office, using an existing and inexpensive waterway and requiring the construction of fairly inexpensive hoverports only. Moreover, many modern suburban housing areas are built close to water while many of the world's newest and most modern airports are built on reclaimed land near the sea.

Take New York City for example. Its three large airports—Kennedy International, Newark Airport, and LaGuardia—are near water. The East River, Hudson River, Long Island Sound, Newark

The ACV at the Expo-67 World's Fair at Montreal, carried visitors to and from the Islands in the St. Lawrence.

Bay, and Upper Bay provide ideal natural hoverways for commuter ACV's. Smaller ACV's, carrying 50 to 100 passengers, could operate from downtown Manhattan to either Newark Airport or La-Guardia.* Larger ACV's, carrying several hundred passengers, could operate in Long Island Sound to cities like Stamford, Connecticut, cities on Long Island itself, or up the Hudson River to Albany. These larger craft could operate through the Verrazzano Narrows to Kennedy International Airport with no bother from either the waves from the open ocean or any debris which might be found in the Narrows.

Such commuting passengers would sit in comfortable bus-like seats and make the trip in half the time of bus, train or car.

For sheltered water operations, where rough seas are not a prob-

*An ACV route using small ACV's from downtown Manhattan to Kennedy International would probably not be economically attractive since the land journey is shorter, and since the smaller ACV's might find Atlantic Ocean operations south of Kennedy International Airport difficult.

lem, the medium size hovercraft is an ideal vehicle. The seating is usually of the airline type or, for very short runs, bus type seating is adequate. Ventilation, heating or air conditioning can be provided as the climate requires. The larger hovercraft on longer runs offer the comforts of snack bars and lounge facilities.

For the traveler who is taking his car with him, the process of embarkation and debarkation is quite simple. He merely drives up a ramp to the parking area of the hovercraft, parks his car under the direction of an attendant, and then walks to the passenger lounge. On arrival at his destination, he simply claims his car and drives off. (See Figure 27.)

Commuter and ferry hovercraft are not without problems, however—noise, vibration and motion. But trains, automobiles and airplanes were not faultless when they first appeared. The internal sound of a hovercraft is a product of engine and propeller noises plus, at high speed, wind howling. Much effort is being expended to minimize this noise problem. Propeller noise is largely caused by the top speed of the moving blades. The nearer to the speed of sound the blade tips come, the more irritating the sound grows because of the higher pitch.

To people living or working alongside the rivers and waterways, this external noise is also a problem.

Driving cars off the English Channel ferry

The Denny Hovercraft—a hybrid vehicle with immersed sidewalls. This may prove to be the most practical commuter ACV for inter-city travel.

Part of the noise problem can be solved by the employment of "hybrid hovercraft"—instead of using exterior propellers, the hybrid hovercraft has either regular water propellers or jet propulsion. Of course, this prevents such a hybrid from being truly amphibious, so it must stay in the water. (See Figure 28.)

Motion, of course, can be a problem for those who tend toward seasickness, and, in the case of people moving about the hovercraft, it can become a matter of safety. Commuter hovercraft do not usually operate where seas are large, but some inland waterway services can still encounter rough water—Puget Sound, San Francisco Bay, Chesapeake Bay, the English Channel, the Kattegat, to name a few. Severe weather can, of course, cause cancellation of service, but this also happens to ordinary ships, ferries and aircraft. In any case, the motion problem of hovercraft is solvable and in time will be no more restrictive than the motion problem of a fast train or a jet aircraft.

It might be of historical interest to record the impressions of some of the 150 newspapermen, magazine writers and radio and TV correspondents who made the maiden journey of the *Princess Margaret* across the English Channel, on July 30, 1968, a 35-minute trip at 50 knots which encountered 4- to 5-foot waves.

Climbing up the aircraft-style ladder, the guests entered an airline-type cabin and sat down in aircraft-type seats. Soon, the four 19-foot propellers came to life. "I felt the craft rise sedately," said one passenger, "all of seven feet. We slipped off the ramp, past the harbor entrance, and were quickly up to 50 knots. It was the fastest and best ride I ever had across the Channel."

But for all who enjoyed the first memorable flight, there were a number who raised objections.

". . . I crossed the Channel yesterday in the world's first car-carrying hovercraft—and it was just like driving over a tank training course."

". . . It was like an arduous flight in a wartime troop aircraft in bumpy weather. The noise, composed of engine whine, ventilation hiss and a deep structural reverberation, made speech difficult."

". . . It's one helluva way to get to Europe, skittering around on the surface of the ocean like a demented water beetle."

". . . It's like a clog dancer, clomping and kicking her way across the Channel."

". . . The hovercraft jidders and lurches like a big jet in moderate air turbulence. She hits the waves like a speeding motorboat, rather than slicking them like a ship. There is no bar, no refreshments, and promenading is discouraged because of the shudder."

Most of the initial passengers, however, were not so cynical and recognized such problems as temporary and to be expected in such a new and untried service.

"It was a bumpy ride, to be sure," said one of the more farsighted writers, "but marine history was made. Never have so many people crossed the Channel so fast in such relative comfort."

To those with vision, indeed, the initial crossing was not expected to be problem-free. Riding across a choppy channel in this

The *Swift* and the *Sure*, the new hovercraft ferries which travel between Ramsgate, England, and Calais, France, are equally navigable on water or on land, as shown in these two pictures.

160-ton water beetle only 9 years after the first hovercraft flight was comparable to having the first automobile only a decade after the invention of the wheel. The reduction of a trip normally two hours long to only forty minutes was a bright promise of things to come, and, in time, the problems of noise, motion and vibration would be easily overcome.

In fact, only one year later, the cross-channel 1969 service was not only swift, but dependable, quiet and comfortable, thanks to improved skirts and enhanced soundproofing. The schedule of the *Swift* and the *Sure*, Ramsgate to Calais hovercraft ferries, during the 1969 season called for twelve trips per day. Thirty cars and 250 passengers were carried per trip, at a top speed of 77 knots, even in 35 mile-per-hour winds. (See Figures 29a and b.)

7

Skimming for Sport

One of the world's fastest growing sports is skimming—certainly it is the newest. Starting in England in 1962, skimming has spread around the world—Canada, Trinidad and Tobago, the United States, Finland, France, Argentina, South Africa, and Australia. All of these countries now have hoverclubs, sporting ACV organizations, amateur "hovernauts," racing events and rallies. Many of these countries also have manufacturing companies building and selling professionally constructed, light ACV's for racing and sporting purposes. (See Figure 30.) The popularity of ACV skimming is doubling every year.

This new fun sport promises great competition for water skiing, surfboarding, skydiving, drag racing, and bike racing. "Building your own ACV" has become a great basement pastime. ACV races and rallies are growing commonplace. In Canada, the United Kingdom and the United States, several companies are now selling small sporting ACV's for prices from $500 to $3,000, and build-your-own kits from $100 up—without the motor, of course.* As the ACV skimming sport becomes increasingly popular, and quantity produc-

*See Appendix 2 for a listing of ACV's or ACV kits, plus engines, which can be purchased.

Franklin Dobson's Light ACV, *UFO-26* is used for racing and sports by an increasing number of private owners. It is available in kit form for do-it-yourself fans.

tion and manufacturing competition rise, lower prices can be expected. Appendix 1 is a list of ACV makers and manufacturers who sell both complete craft and kits.

Sporting ACV's are designed to skim across water, snow, swamps and beaches. They have become popular, not only with sportsmen and racing enthusiasts, but with explorers and those who need to penetrate into areas inaccessible by boats or automobile as well. Hunters and fishermen are finding they can use a sports ACV to travel across swampy land to better hunting and fishing grounds. (See Figure 31.)

One of the unusual thrills of an ACV trip is going from water to land—or vice versa—for you expect to feel a thump . . . but it never comes.

Hovernauts are ecstatic about skimming. For those who have tried it, it is a new sensation, a new thrill. One of the early ACV sporting and manufacturing pioneers is Mr. C. C. Knight of Hoverknights. "Flying an ACV," he said, "is a cross between sailing a boat, flying an aircraft, and driving a car on a sheet of ice!" Another pioneer, Mr. Geoffrey Harding, describes skimming to be like "sliding on a continuous banana skin."

A ride on an ACV is different and unique from any other kind of transportation—smooth and effortless flight across water, and equally exciting trips across beaches and open countryside. In addition to the sensation of speed, the hovernaut gets the feeling of flying, for indeed, he *is* airborne, although only a few inches above the surface. (See Figure 32.)

ACV skimming has the speed and action qualities of flying, surfing and skiing, but it requires more coordination, mechanical skill and technical ability. As with surfing or flying, skimming by a very light ACV requires good body balance and coordination. Remembering that he is riding on top of a big bubble of air, the hovernaut understands that a shift of his weight to one side tends to slide him off the top of the bubble, so he moves toward the direction in which he is leaning—that is, toward the top of the bubble once more. This process is called kinesthetics.

The Aero-Go Sports ACV, "Terra Skipper," a fiberglass single seat, experimental air cushion vehicle, built to develop engine and control configurations.

Skimming has many sporting advantages—it is as fast as many types of vehicular racing. It is less expensive than water skiing, if you must buy your own tow boat. Skimming can be done in shallow water areas where a skiing boat cannot go. It is not as dangerous as skydiving or bike racing and it can be done by more kinds of people. Actual skimming racing includes speed tests, similar to Le-Mans or Indianapolis, but other races may include obstacle courses, slalom courses, and amphibious contests over land and water, all timed against the clock. (See Figure 33.)

Learning to Operate an ACV.

According to Mr. John Vass, one of the earliest operators of ACV's and a well known figure in the ACV sporting field, most people can learn good control of a light hovercraft in about four hours.

"The most important point to remember," he says, "is that, once the air cushion is inflated and the thrust engine is turning, things happen quickly—and these things must be controlled—or they can become unpleasant or painful."

The Cushion Flight 240, one of the popular sports ACV's by Ralph P. Maloof, makes an ideal fishing craft—and a land vehicle, too.

The Hover-Air is a popular English ACV, used by harbor police, customs officials, coastal engineers, fisheries personnel, etc.

First Lesson

Let us suppose you have built your own ACV. For your first lesson, take your hovercraft to a large, flat, uncluttered piece of ground, preferably one that is grassy. Make any spectators or helpers stay clear. Start the engine and run up the power until you fill your air cushion. On your first hop, don't try to maneuver—just get the feel of the air bubble on which you are sitting.

When you throttle down, note how long it takes your air bubble to deflate or decay. This period of delay is important because it gives you some idea as to how fast and within what distance you can stop your ACV.

Second Lesson

For your second lesson, after you are riding confidently on your air cushion, practice learning. Remember, this is called kinesthetics in hovercraft language. Lean to one side or the other without changing the power setting and see what happens. Next, try leaning forward. Note that as the nose or bow of your hovercraft goes down, it will start to move forward. This is because air is escaping from the rear, or after skirt of your machine, and this escape "pushes" your ACV forward. Practice moving your hovercraft forward, sideways and diagonally by kinesthetics.

Third Lesson

For your third lesson, start moving around your grassy tryout field and practice turning—but keep the speed low—about 10 mph. Apply your turning controls and make a slow, large circle. Continue this, gradually increasing power and speed. Mastering turns is a *must*—and remember that turning in a wind is quite a different matter than turning in calm air! When you have learned to turn at low speeds, you can begin trying high speed turns—but be careful! Depending on your particular machine, it is possible to "lean" so much that you may "spin out" and overturn.

Fourth Lesson

Next, find a plot of ground which has a slight incline and notice the performance of your ACV. If your vehicle is a powerful one, you should be able to climb a one-in-ten slope.* Of course, if you get a "running start," you can climb a steeper grade. Go up the slope—then let the craft slide straight backwards down to the foot. During the learning stage, it is better to avoid trying to turn around on a slope. Let this come later. Also, don't try coming down slopes *sideways* until you are expert.

These are the first four general lessons and they will vary, depending on the power and size of your ACV. After you have learned to master them (in about four hours), you can begin more ambitious training such as the following:

Turning Stops

The fastest way to stop a light ACV which is up to speed is to make a "twissle" turn. (It is also easiest on the skirts and skids of the

---

*A one-in-ten slope means that for every ten feet of distance, the ground rises one foot.

vehicle.) This involves turning the hovercraft while in motion, so that the opposing thrust overcomes the momentum. In high winds, however, this can be a difficult, even dangerous procedure—so be careful! Hovercraft have been known to somersault.

Spin Turn

After you are up to speed, apply your turning control full force, and you will induce a two or three G turn** as you make a tight "bank." When you have become a *real* expert, it is possible to make a 360° turn of your ACV while continuing on your original course!

Rough Terrain

Don't tackle rough terrain, bumps, ditches, curbs, etc., until you have *thoroughly* mastered your machine. Once you have learned its capabilities, you will know what terrain you can and cannot cross.

Transitions

Assuming that your ACV is an amphibian and designed for both land and water travel, moving from overland to over water or vice versa is simple if the beach gradient is slight. Make your first transition at right angles to the shoreline. Furthermore, it is best to remain in shallow water until you are expert in water maneuvers. Do not tackle choppy water or surf until you have acquired considerable experience.

Water Skimming

At slow speeds, your ACV will act very much like a boat, but after it achieves "hump speed" (see page 5, Figure 1, Chapter 1), it becomes a hydroplane, with you skipping across the water. At first, the ACV's nose will come up slightly, then, as you increase speed, it will flatten out again. Don't try fancy or tight turns at first. You may find it takes a greater distance to turn around at the same

---

**G is a unit which measures acceleration. One G is the acceleration due to gravity at the surface of the earth, approximately 32.2 feet per second.

speed on water than it does on land. Remember the wind factor—turning downwind may be difficult. It is prudent to keep your speed low until you've had about two hours practice. Be careful of the wake of other boats—avoid them at first, and, if necessary, either slow down and go "hullborne," or else cross the other boat's wake at a 45° angle. (See Figure 34.)

Equipment

If you are skimming on land, it is wise to wear a hardhat or crash helmet. Goggles are also advisable. On sand, or in dirt, goggles are a *must* if you are to see clearly. Do not wear a loose hat or scarves, etc., which can be blown off and ingested into your fan or propeller. On water journeys, wear a life jacket. If high speed is your cup of tea, you should wear both a safety belt and shoulder straps.

Licensing Your ACV

In the United States, all sporting ACV's are presently classified as boats. Therefore, if you plan to operate your ACV in any water area which comes under USCG jurisdiction, you must have your ACV registered with U.S. Coast Guard. In many states, you must also be registered with their small craft divisions or harbor bureaus, in the same manner as any power boat. Depending on the size and power of your ACV, it may also have to pass U.S. Coast Guard requirements for construction, safety and equipment. See Chapter 9 for details.

The Fan Jet Skimmer—an inexpensive sports ACV by Melville Beardsley also available in kit form.

In England, you must obtain a Certificate of Test and Inspection for light hovercraft from the Hover Club of Great Britain, issued in collaboration with the Air Registration Board.

In the United States, if you expect to join a club or participate in rallies, you should join the National Association of Air Cushion Vehicle Enthusiasts, 2912 Andros Street, Costa Mesa, California, 92626. Your membership will include a monthly newsletter, technical help, safety standards for building and operating ACV's, club rules for racing.

Insuring Your ACV

There are three principal companies now handling ACV insurance:

> USA — Insurance Forum of Long Beach
> 4014 Long Beach Blvd., Suite 112
> Long Beach, California 90807
>
> England — Green Street Insurance Ltd.
> Insurance Brokers
> 125 Felstead Road
> Orpington, Kent
>
> Canada — Marsh and McLennon, Ltd.
> Place Villa Marie
> Montreal, 2, Quebec

ACV Clubs

The three largest clubs associated with sporting and private ACV's are as follows:

> USA — National Association for Air Cushion
> Vehicle Enthusiasts, Inc. (NAACE)
> 2912 Andros Street
> Costa Mesa, California 92627

Canada — Experimental Hovercraft Association (EHA)
Suite 25, 15 Esterbrooke Avenue
Willowdale, Ontario, Canada

England — Hover Club of Great Britain, Limited
12 Lind Street
Ryde, Isle of Wight

Rallies and Races

Among the most popular aspects of ACV sport skimming are the
rallies and races that are held—sometimes for prizes or money, sometimes just for fun and pleasure. (See Figure 35.)

Whatever the goal, the rallies are informal and each one is different—different courses, lengths, obstacles and conditions. A typical
race might involve any or all of the following—a distance run (for
speed), an obstacle course (around markers), a run across a section
of water or lake, a run across hummocks or mounds, a run through
a gate or opening, a run up and down an incline, a run around a
specially marked circle, a run across varying terrain of increasing
difficulty—concrete, grass, a plowed field, sand, weeds, logs, and
water. Any or all of these features may be included. No standard-
ized "race" or track has yet been created.

In the few short years of ACV racing, a body of rules has grown
and been accepted. The recognized referees and arbiters of these
rules are combined in a "council" representing the various clubs of
the countries which have hover clubs.

First of all, this Council establishes broad categories or classes for
ACV competition such as these: (1) ACV's operated only over
ground or exclusively amphibious ACV's, (2) propeller-driven
ACV's, jet-driven ACV's, or "other" power, (3) pure ACV's, (air
cushion only) or ground-touching ACV's, (4) homemade ACV's
or professionally built ACV's.

Other methods of classifying the sporting ACV are by overall
size (length, width, total weight, etc.) and by engine capacity (as
measured by the cubic centimeters of engine cylinder displacement,

The first North American sports ACV rally in North America, held at Abbotsford, Canada, in August, 1968. From top to bottom they are Cushion Flight 240, "Flower Pot Special," and Fan Jet Skimmer.

or recognized horsepower measurement). In most cases, the competing ACV's must be used solely for recreational or sporting purposes.

At the present time, the Council of Hover Clubs has subdivided the sporting ACV's as follows:

(1) Engine rating .... (a) one class *above* 500 cc capacity

(b) one class *below* 500 cc capacity

(2) Type of
Propulsion .... (a) Propeller Driven
1 Over 500 cc
2 Under 500 cc
(b) Air Jet Driven
1 Over 500 cc
2 Under 500 cc
(c) "Other Propulsion" (This would include special types of ACV's which use wheels, or other ground-touching methods of propulsion, in which part of the weight is ground-borne rather than air cushion-borne).

(3) Weight .... The United States has no weight limitations at present. Canada limits sporting ACV's to 3,000 pounds, and no horsepower limitation. Great Britain specifies a maximum weight of 2,000 pounds, 80 brake horsepower, and no more than two persons, including the operator.

Using the above broad guidelines, the committee for an individual race or rally will determine what types of ACV's will compete in their particular contest and they will probably use the handicapping system also developed by the Council of Hover Clubs.

Here is how the handicap system works. Let us assume that the race judges have announced several categories of competition—and one category will be for propeller-driven ACV's with engines under 500 cc's. Let's also assume that three contestants show up on the announced rally day—let's call them Tom, Dick and Harry.

The race course has been established—through a starting gate, across an open grassy field for 500 yards, a turn of 90°, up a hummock and down the other side, another 90° turn, in and out of a series of rubber markers for 100 yards, through a 25-foot-wide gate, another turn, across a pond of water 50 yards wide, up a slight grade across a sand pit, and onto the final stretch, again a 500-yard run over a grassy field to the finish line.

In advance of the actual race, after looking at the course, Tom, Dick and Harry one after the other, make a trial or first run. Tom does it in 5 minutes, 10 seconds; Dick does it in 6 minutes flat, and Harry zips around the course in 4 minutes, 35 seconds. By averaging these three times, an average of 5 minutes and 15 seconds becomes "par"—that is, the time to beat.

For the actual race, each competitor will be given 500 points before he starts. If he runs the course in exactly "par" time, 5'15", he keeps his 500 points and that is his score. But if Tom beats par time by 10 seconds, for example, he gets a point for each second saved—and a score of 510. If Dick does it in 5'25", or 10 seconds *slower* than "par," he loses 10 points and his score is 490. If Harry does it again in 4'35", he gets a final score of 525 and is the winner for the "heat."

If more than one race is participated in by the contestants over the same course, each individual's several scores are averaged.

The driver with the highest final score, of course, is the winner.

Besides the thrill and excitement of skimming competition, there is one larger result of amateur racing and rallies. It is display of individual ingenuity and resourcefulness at such events by dedicated amateurs which fuels the worthwhile progress and advancement of the entire ACV commercial and military industry.

8

The Legal Problems
of ACV's

The development and use of ACV's in so many fields of human endeavor and in so many countries has happened so rapidly that lawyers, judges, insurance companies and legislators have been unable to catch up. With hovercraft already hauling thousands of passengers and tons of freight every month, with ACV water taxis and ACV ferry systems springing up in several major cities and harbors of the world, with the sporting ACV craze moving into high gear, the need to define, regulate, certify and legislate concerning ACV's has become a matter of great urgency. But solving the many vexing legal problems that have arisen is not easy. For example:

> —if a hovercraft collides with a boat, do the rules of the air or the rules of the sea apply?
> —does a hovercraft floating down a highway have a right to be there?
> —is a hovercraft an airplane, a ship, or a helicopter—or all three?
> —does a hovercraft abide by the recognized maritime rules of the road or by Air Traffic Control regulations?

—does a hovercraft have to have a license? If so, which kind?

—does a hovernaut have to have a driver's permit, a pilot's license or a Coast Guard marine operator's certificate?

—if you build your own hovercraft, do the construction, materials and safety equipment have to be those of an airplane or a ship?

—do the existing laws pertaining to aircraft noise apply to a hovercraft?

—does an amphibious ACV, able to travel either on land or sea, have to have headlights, tail lights and turning signals or should it have red and green navigational running lights—or both?

—for tax purposes, is a hoverpad or hoverterminal an airfield or a pier?

These are but a few of the many knotty legal problems which are now being examined in legislation. In the United Kingdom, a hovercraft bill is currently under study. In Canada and in the United States, preliminary legislation is being formulated. In the United Nations, a special Inter-Governmental Maritime Consultative Organization has been considering the legal problem of ACV's for more than a year.

Legally, the problem begins with definition—the very problem

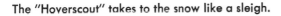
The "Hoverscout" takes to the snow like a sleigh.

The "Trident" means fun for a boy because it is so easy to handle.

the author stressed in Chapter One. How to define "it" and what to call "it"—and neither problem is easily or simply answered.

How *not* to define an ACV is easy. In the United States, the Federal Aviation Agency has said ACV's are *not* aircraft. The U.S. Coast Guard classes any ACV as a boat—whether or not it uses the water. The International Civil Aviation Organization (ICAO), an agency of the United Nations, took positive action to redefine the word *aircraft* to *exclude* hovercraft and air cushion vehicles. Formerly, ICAO defined an aircraft as "any machine that can derive support in the atmosphere from the reaction of the air." When hovercraft came along, ICAO changed the definition by adding the words "other than the reaction of the air against the earth's surface."

Therefore, as far as the ICAO is concerned (and most nations which operate commercial aircraft are ICAO members), the ACV is *not* an airplane.

Does *not* being an airplane automatically make the hovercraft a ship? Not necessarily. In Britain and Canada, hovercraft are classed as aircraft. But Japan, the United States, France, Italy, Sweden, and Norway have all taken the position that ACV's are ships.

Sir Christopher Cockerell was pretty close to the answer to "what is it" in his original patent application, when he titled his invention: "Improvements in or relating to vehicles for traveling over land and/or water."

After a decade of indecision, however, it seems clear that legal experts around the world are about ready to agree that:

1. The ACV/hovercraft is *not* an airplane.
2. The larger ACV's/hovercraft are becoming more and more like ships (certainly the ones used in commerce, ferry and tranport operations are).
3. Smaller ACV/hovercraft are special—neither ship nor airplane.

It is to be hoped that all nations will finally agree on what "it" is—for the situation would be terribly messy if some nations continue to classify ACV's as *airplanes* and other nations call the same vehicles *ships*!

At the moment, from a legal standpoint, the *definition* most generally accepted is this one, taken from clause 4(1) of the United Kingdom Hovercraft Bill, now pending in the House of Commons:

"Hovercraft means a vehicle which is designed to be supported when in motion wholly or partly by air expelled from the vehicle to form a cushion of which the boundaries include the ground, water or other surface beneath the vehicle."

Note that the word "vehicle" is used three times in this definition.

Note also the word "hovercraft" in the above definition. The United Kingdom prefers the word; *the United States does not—* although our government hasn't made up it mind *which* word or words *should* be used.

What difference, you ask, does all this fuss over what you call them or how you define them really make? A very great deal of difference, indeed, as has been indicated earlier in this chapter.

If ACV's are legally determined to be ships, they would then come under The Hague Rules concerning shipping, which govern insurance, liability, transportation of goods, and safety—and, of course, they would then be subject to Admiralty law. On the other hand, if they are legally classed as aircraft, then a very different set

This SRN4 "Mountbatten" Hovercraft is used for ferry service across the English Channel, carrying 250 passengers and 30 automobiles.

of international laws and regulations would apply. Insuring the life of an air passenger, or air cargo, for example, is much more expensive than insuring a passenger or cargo carried on a ship.

Moreover, if a hovercraft is classed as a ship, it will have to abide by certain regulations as to how it is constructed, or what materials, what safety equipment it must carry, what tests it must pass, etc. If it is classed as an aircraft, different standards will apply.

In another decade, hopefully, these legal snarls will all be untangled, but there is no doubt that ACV/hovercraft—or whatever word the world finally settles on—are going to change the face of surface transportation. In crowded harbors, and in ocean channels in and out of harbors, some changes will have to be made in rules of the road for these "flying ships" of tomorrow, capable of 60 to 100 knots speed. Perhaps there will have to be one ship channel in crowded harbors for conventional slow ships and a special "hover channel" for the ACV's. In the open ocean, perhaps special lanes will have to be designated for the big, 100-knot ACV's and CAB's of tomorrow. Certainly, there will be a special body of rules and regulations, internationally accepted, which will apply to high-speed ships which fly and recognize them for what they are—a new, distinctive and unique form of transport.

9

Industrial and Utility
Uses of ACV's

In Chapter 1, two practical and early applications of the air cushion principle were mentioned—the Hoover vacuum cleaner which "floats" itself from room to room to provide easy cleaning by the housewife, and the "floating" 400-pound refrigerator which can be moved away from the wall for practically effortless cleaning beneath it.

As amphibious and waterborne transport type ACV's were developed, there were associated developments, leading to commercial, industrial and utility applications which have proven practical and which show even greater promise.

Take the problem of moving a 490-passenger, 160-ton Boeing 747 jumbo jet airliner, for example. If such a huge aircraft must be moved under its own power, it uses expensive quantities of fuel, even though it does reduce valuable ground maintenance time. On the other hand, maneuvering the jumbo jets into and out of maintenance hangars with tractors is tough, tedious and time consuming.

The answer to this transportation problem is a form of ACV air cushion castor platform or turntable which can literally "float" the heavy airliner across concrete aprons, taxiways and hangar floors.

This same principle will allow an aircraft to be "swung" in a circle, in order to calibrate its navigational instruments and equipment. (See Figure 36.)

These ACV pallets have a variety of commercial trade names— Aero-Caster, Aeroglide, Aeroveyors, Floataload, Airfloat, Hoverpallet, Jetveyor and Flying Carpet. All, however, use the same ACV principles described in Chapter 1.

Figure 37 is a diagrammatic sketch. Air is pumped into a pallet or platform, and escapes through a thin, lubricating seal or disc made of plastic or fabric material. Under pressure, these seals assume a doughnut shape and, as the pressurized air seeps out, the heavy weight becomes "airborne" and can be pushed, pulled, or moved with ease. Of course, the floor must be solid, flat, level and clean, and for some applications, a damp or wet floor tends to lubricate the leading edge of the doughnuts as they move.

Figure 38 is an example of how the air source from a regular household vacuum cleaner, powering an ACV pallet, can lift an 1800-pound Volkswagen. Figure 39 shows how a five-ton machine can be moved on four such ACV pallets. Any type of bulky or

A Boeing 747 being "rotated" by means of ACV pallets.

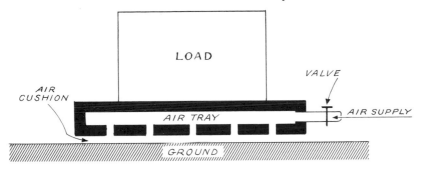

ACV pallet enabling loads to be moved over any flat surface

heavy equipment can be transported by these pallets—machinery within a factory, equipment in a hospital, heavy containers in a warehouse.

There are numberless uses with specific applications. For example, the U.S. Navy can use ACV pallets for moving huge ship propellers around shipyards. The National Broadcasting Company has bought air bearing platforms in order to transfer bleacher sections around a studio. Figure 40 shows a huge oil storage tank being re-sited with the help of an ACV skirt. As indicated in this picture,

Floating a Volkswagen on an ACV pallet powered by a household vacuum cleaner

Moving a five-ton shovel by means of ACV pallets

A seventy-ton fuel tank being moved by an ACV skirt

The Hospital Hoverbed

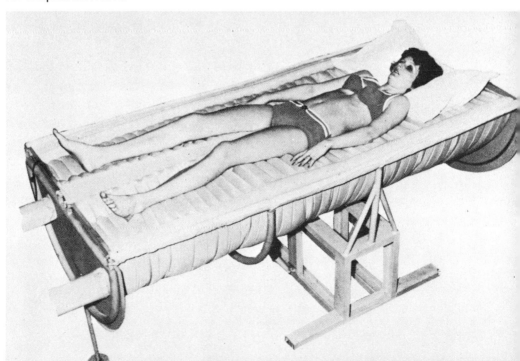

two Esso fuel tanks, each 50 feet in diameter and weighing 70 tons, were moved 200 yards over a zigzag path to a new site. The skirts were specially made for the job. Air pumped in at 60 pounds per square foot lifted the tanks 7 inches off the ground.

The principal advantage of hoverpallets is their ruggedness and simplicity. Through their use, heavy loads can be moved with minimum effort; there is a reduction of the headroom required; loads can be carried over weak floors; the noise level is low; standard air hoses can be used; etc. Most important, they are economical.

A novel idea for a hoverplatform that has been tried in England is the "Hoverlauncher." This is a boat launcher, designed to carry sailing boats from a parking ramp across mudflats and shallow water and deposit them in deep water. The boat launcher is utilized when boat trailers can be used only with difficulty or cannot be used at all.

Another worthwhile application is the "Hoverbed," used success-fully for patients with severe burns. (See Figure 41.) This consists of a rigid frame inside of which a light nylon-coated bag is hung. The top of the bag is formed by two rows of pockets, similar to the segmented skirts of a hovercraft. Warm, sterile air at low pressure ($\frac{1}{4}$ to $\frac{1}{3}$ pound per square inch) is pumped into the bag, inflating the pockets.

The patient is placed on the bed, and the pockets form a seal along the sides of the body, while the main part of the body is sup-ported by air (except for the head).

Two burned patients have used this hoverbed. The first one had gasoline burns over one-third of his body, front and back. The second patient had been burning wastepaper in a windstorm which ignited the oily clothes he was wearing. He received extensive burns on his side. In the first case, the patient was left in the hover-bed for six hours, the second for fifteen-and-a-half hours, almost completely out of touch with the bedding. Doctors reported in both cases that the weeping areas of the burns dried very rapidly and nursing care was improved.

Figure 42 is still another application of ACV platforms. Sections

Moving a twelve-ton section of air-lubricated stadium seating by hand

of seats can be repositioned by tractors to convert a stadium's seating arrangement from football to baseball or to horseracing in a matter of hours.

One application still in the development stage which looks promising is the "Helibarge." (See Figure 43.) This vehicle is designed so that a helicopter can land in the center opening, then lift and move the entire platform, using the down wash of the helo rotors to provide the cushion. The structure itself would find uses as the transportation of mobile hospitals in war zones, employment as supply barges, or as oil exploration platforms in swampy terrain.

Another very promising field for the ACV principle will be toys of all descriptions—and rides in amusement parks.

Still another utility use of ACV's is in the agricultural area of crop spraying. The Canadians tried a Bertin/Sedan BC Terraplane in June, 1967, at the Department of Agriculture experimental farm at Ottawa, Canada. Figure 44 is an example of an agricultural ACV. Gunderson in Minnesota has designed a crop sprayer which can spray a 32-foot swath of farmland at a speed of 15 mph, and, at this

The Helicopter "helibarge"

The Gunderson Agricultural ACV is used for crop spraying

speed, will cover eight acres with only twenty gallons of spray.

As for conventional ACV's themselves, many utility applications other than passenger transport have already been demonstrated successfully.

One large oil company employs an ACV to service and supply its offshore drilling rigs.

The Indian government uses a hovercraft to stop smuggling out of Dubai, in the Gulf of Arabia. In a three-month period, three captures were made. One shipment contained more than $250,000 in gold. Another motorized dhow was captured with a $100,000 cargo of contraband textiles. Perhaps the smugglers will now start using hovercraft themselves?

The Cunard Steamship Company, Limited, carries an ACV on one of its bigger ships, to use in harbor runs and taking passengers on sightseeing jaunts at ports of call.

Some airports have found that ACV's are excellent crash rescue craft, as well as firefighting vehicles for those accidents which occur in their vicinity on the water, mudflats and swamps which surround many airfields.

The city of London has bought one hovercraft to fight fires adjacent to the Thames River, using the river water.

The potential uses of ACV's are endless. For example, a specially equipped hovercraft would make an ideal platform for hydrographic survey work, increasing the speed of surveying very greatly. Because of its shallow draft when hullborne, it would be able to work in shallow water regions, as well as in deep water.

The use of ACV's in the Arctic should be mentioned. The trials carried out by Canada in 1966 and 1968 clearly demonstrate the hovercraft's potential in areas of tundra and sea ice under varying snow conditions and during the very difficult river breakup hazards in the springtime.

In March, 1965, an SK-5 hovercraft made a wintertime crossing of Lake Erie, a journey of 235 miles.

In January, 1968, an SR.N6 operated at Churchill, Manitoba, for a ten-week cold weather trial, evaluating its operations over land,

The SRN-6 travels over the ice in Canada

water and ice. This hovercraft was not extensively modified—only additional radios and heaters were added. The SN.R6, unprotected and without benefit of hangar, functioned satisfactorily for the whole time in temperatures as low as −40°F, even in "white out" blizzard conditions. (See Figure 45.)

The following winter, Canada's Centre for Inland Waters used an SK-5 hovercraft to check the chemical, biological and thermal status of Lake Erie, during the height of the winter, something never before tried. While engaged in this project, the SK-5 encountered such massive fields of jagged ice that a helicopter was used as a guide. Even so, the hovercraft managed an average speed of 30 mph and was able, by stopping and boring holes through the ice, to obtain the necessary samples.

As pointed out before, in recently developing countries such as those found in Africa and South America, where access by river is feasible, the ACV can be a means of providing high speed, mobile medical and dental facilities in river areas, some of which may be non-navigable by other types of boats.

Among the most unique applications of the ACV principle are

heavy lift transporters—the truck type ACV. These are used for moving heavy machinery such as 200-ton transformers. In one instance, a 200-ton heavy lift transformer was moved across an old bridge, the capacity of which was only 155 tons! Because heavy lift ACV's could spread the weights evenly by the air cushion, such loads can be moved across bridges which otherwise would have to be strengthened or rebuilt to avoid a detour. In this instance, the British Electricity Generating Board estimated that the ACV heavy lift transporter (which cost $168,000) saved $80,000 on every transformer movement. The same Board has ordered 10-ton ACV loaders for performing off-road maintenance on power lines, thereby avoiding churning up farmland with heavy duty trucks.

The ACV truck, or wheeled hover platform, as some call it, is still another variant of this technique. (See Figure 46.) The air cushions support between 70 percent and 95 percent of the loaded vehicle's weight. Moreover, the weight is distributed over the entire ground or water surface at a very low average bearing weight. The ACV truck can, if required, operate in regular traffic (at 30-35 mph) like any other truck, but it can also negotiate open water, mud, or loose soil. (See Figure 47.) Again, the most obvious use of such ACV trucks is in those sparsely settled areas of the globe which lack developed transportation systems.

Lastly, the ACV trains—also called air trains, aerotrains, and

The ACV truck "Terraplane"—the "truck that can go anywhere"—on road in France

The ACV truck takes to the water

aeroglides—promise to revolutionize the ordinary railroad train. The air trains differ from nautical ACV's (which, of course, are untracked) in that they require tracks. The principle is the same, though. The tracked ACV trains will provide high speed passenger transport in silence and safety along routes that require a minimum of ground space. (See Figures 48 and 49.)

The ACV train promises relief for congested inter-city runs of distances less than 150 miles. Above this distance, the airplane is more competitive. Operating at speeds up to 150 to 200 mph, the ACV train will be unbeatable in terms of speed and service. Riding astride an elevated track, which will be supported on slender pylons, the air train will whiz between cities, or between a city and its airport. Because they can accelerate and brake rapidly on their air cushions, the individual cars will run only 30 seconds apart, carrying as many as 10,000 passengers per hour.

Air trains will someday be powered by the still-in-development linear engine. This is an electric motor with a *flat*, rather than a

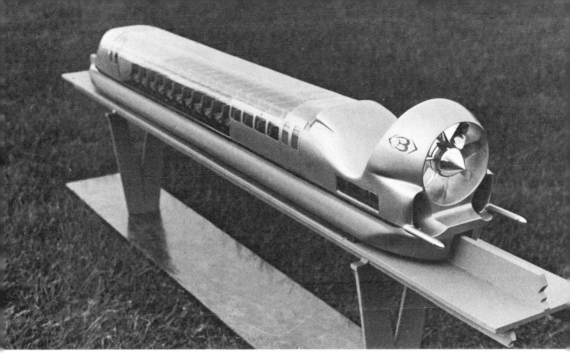

An ACV train model by Bertin of France

The high speed ACV train of tomorrow (Sedam, Paris)

circular, magnetic field. The armature of the motor does not rotate but is propelled along a straight line—hence the word "linear." Such a motor would be perfect for an ACV train. The metal track would provide the magnetic field while the belly of the ACV train would act as the armature, theoretically able to provide swift, silent speeds up to 500 mph.

These are some of the many uses and ideas which the ACV revolution has already produced. When one recalls that the first practical use of ACV's only took place about ten years ago, it can be expected that the large number of utility and industrial uses which have already appeared are but a small sample of the many new and novel—and practical—applications which will be seen in the immediate years ahead.

10

The Captured
Air Bubble Ship

There can be little doubt that the rapid growth and success of the ACV's and hovercraft were a great spur and incentive to marine engineers and ship designers which has led to an intense interest in the Captured Air Bubble ship (CAB). Indeed, so great has been the CAB activity that there is every reason to believe that large, ocean-going ships will be "flying" the Atlantic within the next twenty-five years, perhaps sooner, at speeds of 75 to 100 knots.

In this age of electronic miracles, space travel and moon exploration, the conventional seagoing cargo ship is like a prehistoric monster. Except for nuclear propulsion in a very small number of merchant ships, plus improved building techniques, which have given us both bigger and safer ships, the appearance and operating methods of ocean-going cargo vessels have not changed radically since 1820, when steam replaced sail. The lowly freighters, the turtles of the oceans, still slowly push their way through wind and wave, just as they did more than 100 years ago.

But the little Cockerell balsa wood ACV model, sputtering its noisy path around the basement floor of Whitehall in 1956, is

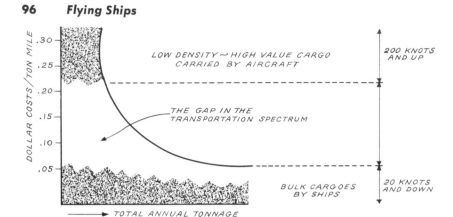

The Gap in Overseas Transportation

changing that maritime situation. Thanks to the hovercraft/ACV development, a new breed of exciting, different, and entirely new ships is about to join man's twentieth century parade of progress.

There's a ready place awaiting these craft now—an empty gap to be filled—as shown in Figure 50. Between the 20-knot sea freighter and the 200-knot air cargo airplane there is a big gap. It is this which the CAB's of tomorrow will fill.

In Chapter 1, how CAB's work was explained. To quickly refresh the reader, the captured air bubble ship is a marine vessel, not an amphibian, in which the air bubble is trapped by slender, solid sidewalls—something akin to twin keel boards—and flexible seals or skirts at the ends of the ship, which extend into the water and allow very little air to escape. Hence, the air bubble is "captured."

The only true CAB vessels now in existence are two experimental craft: the 10-ton XR-1A, made by the U.S. Naval Air Development Center, at Johnsville, Pennsylvania (Figure 51), and the 15-ton XR-3 (Figure 52). The 15-ton HR-3 has recently been converted to gas turbine and redesignated the XR-18.

The nearest ACV type craft to the true CAB which is currently in actual operation is the Denny Sidewall and the Hovermarine HM2 (See Figure 54.)

The XRN-1A, a ten-ton experimental CAB made by the United States Navy

The XR-3, another United States Navy experimental CAB

The XR-1B, a sixteen-ton experimental CAB, powered by gas turbines and propelled by water jets

In 1961, the U.S. Maritime Commission sponsored a research program for high speed ships. The Booz Allen Applied Research Company, of Bethesda, Maryland, was asked to take a ten-year look-ahead at the future of "flying" ships as they might be in the 1970's. This company did so, selected five advanced ship types, and in 1964 picked the CAB as the most promising one.

In 1966, forty expert volunteers from the maritime and shipbuilding field were assembled by the U.S. Department of Commerce to review this study and to look at futuristic ocean-going ships—all of the "its." The forty men were divided into five panels, and the report they produced* kicked off the first organized examination of high speed ocean commerce that had ever been taken on the national level. This panel generally concurred with the Booz Allen report—and also recommended that a 100-ton experimental CAB be built.

From these efforts, a joint committee was formed in 1966, which united the Department of Commerce and the U.S. Navy in a common effort, resulting in the Joint Surface-Effect Ship Project Office (JSESPO).

In March, 1969, contracts were negotiated by the JSESPO

*"Surface Effect Ships for Ocean Commerce"

The Hovermarine HM-2 Sidewall passing under Tower Bridge, London

The Aerojet CAB, now under construction, will test the sea-worthiness of 5000-ton, ocean-going captured air bubble ships

with Aerojet General Corporation and Bell Aerosystems Corporation for construction of two 90-100 ton test craft, which will serve as test beds for a 500-ton experimental ship, with a 4000- to 5000-ton, 80-knot surface effect ship to follow.

The Aerojet CAB (Figure 55) will be 82 feet long and 42 feet wide, and will use gas turbines for the power plants. The propulsion will be water jets, not propellers, and the captured air bubble will be supplied by fans. The ship will be built at the Tacoma Boat Building Company, in Tacoma, Washington, and testing is to be conducted in Puget Sound.

The Bell CAB (Figure 56) will be 78 feet long and 35 feet wide. The hull will be welded marine aluminum, with two side walls extending nearly the length of the hull and flexible bow and stern seals. The control cabin will be mounted aft on the centerline and will accommodate a crew of four, both operating and living space. Eight lift fans will generate the air cushion, while propulsion will be supplied by a pair of super-cavitating propellers. The Bell craft will be built in New Orleans, Louisiana.

The target date for the delivery of the CAB ships, the Aerojet and the Bell, is 30 June 1970.

From these experimental CAB's will come the design for a 4000- to 5000-ton ship. The two smaller ships will be given a great number of tests and trials before the big ships are produced. For example, we do not know how well a 5,000- or 10,000-ton ship might perform in rough seas. Presently, all our information is theoretical. We do know that the North Atlantic in the winter is perhaps the world's worst ocean. Ten per cent of the time, waves average 34 feet in height, while they are 17 feet high one-third of the time. This means two things—CAB ships will have to be tough to operate in such seas, or else they will have to avoid the rough seas by skirting the storm areas.

For such flying craft, we are not certain of what changes in ship construction methods will be required. We have no knowledge of how comfortable or safe it will be for passengers who might travel in them. Suppose a 100-knot ship loses power and suddenly decelerates? An abrupt stop might prove very difficult for passengers—and the galley dishes! We have no knowledge of how these CAB's will handle in a harbor at low speeds, or precisely how they will handle at sea at high speeds. Another unknown is what effect strong crosswinds might have on their slender sidewalls, or

The Bell CAB, a 100-ton surface effect ship (SES) is being designed for speeds in excess of 80 knots

how much safety equipment must be built in them. Finally, what stresses will be placed on a 5000- and 10,000-ton ship, traveling over a choppy ocean at 100 knots is unknown—especially on the bow and stern "flexible seals" or "skirts." All this is only guess-work now.

Therefore, through the Bell and Aerojet test-bed, 100-ton ships will provide answers to some of these—and a thousand more—questions. Figures 69 and 70 are artist's sketches which will give some idea of what such a 100-knot CAB ship of the 1980's and 1990's might look like.

By 1990, despite all the present problems and unknowns, CAB ships will certainly be "flying" across the Atlantic—"flying" in the sense that they will be riding an air bubble and "flying" in the sense they will be making 100 knots.

Why is there so much enthusiasm for the CAB? Here are its advantages:

1. *Speed* .... 60 to 80 knots is feasible for the first generation ship, 100 knots for the next.

2. *Size* .... 4,000 to 5,000 tons first generation ships, bigger in succeeding generations.

3. *Construction* .... All metal construction is feasible, except possibly for fore and aft skirt bubble seals.

4. *Propulsion* .... The design of CAB ships will allow a variety of propulsion types—jet/prop on top, super-cavitating propeller or water jet. This will be discussed further below.

5. *Type of Power* .... Because of the very high-power requirements, high-speed CAB ships will probably use some of the new propulsion systems now in development, such as gas-turbine propulsion

or nuclear propulsion or perhaps a combination. In the latter, a nuclear plant would be employed for cruising, while the gas-turbine would be used for high speed dashes. This combination is promising for combatant CAB's.

6. *Military* .... The promise of high speed will permit CAB combat ships to better avoid submarine attack. Also, at 80- to 100-knot cruise speed, with side walls at minimum draft, the risk of torpedo hits or damage is reduced, since they will be only several inches under the water's surface. This will be further discussed in Chapter 11.

7. *Cargo* .... The CAB lends itself to automated, preloaded cargo containers, which will maximize fast turnarounds.

8. *Fast Stops* .... Most marine engineers agree that stopping a CAB in a short distance will be relatively easy—simply dump the captured bubble and let the ship settle deeper into the water. But it might not be very comfortable for the passengers or their cars!

9. *Crew Manning* .... CAB's will require fewer but better trained sailors than conventional ships.

Disadvantages:

1. CAB's will require tremendous amounts of propulsive power. This is so important it will be discussed below.
2. Draft of ship, "off-bubble," may be greater than a conventional ship because of depth of slender side walls.

3. The length-beam ratio will be higher than for an ordinary ship. Therefore, handling and docking of wide CAB ships may be a problem. For example, width and depth of river channels, bridge widths, etc., may limit inner harbor use.
4. Development costs will be high.
5. High speeds at sea will cause some drastic changes in the Rules of the Road. As mentioned in Chapter 8, certain difficult legal problems are foreseen.

The U.S. Navy has done some studies which show the tremendous power requirement for ocean-going CAB's. For comparison, remember that an 80,000-ton Forrestal class aircraft carrier has a power plant of about 300,000 horsepower, giving her a top speed of something more than 30 knots. The David Taylor Model Basin studies show that a 12,500 ton CAB ship, able to navigate in seven-foot seas at 65 knots, will require 315,000 horsepower! For the same ship to attain 100 knots would require 420,000 horsepower! You can see, therefore, that, unless nuclear power is used, the CAB ship will need to carry a lot of fuel! And reliable, safe, *lightweight* nuclear power plants have not yet been built.

One of the attractions of a large, ocean-going CAB ship is the possible use of water jet propulsion rather than propellers. Water jets give such advantages as less noise (important against enemy submarines), curtailed propeller damage and entanglement, and reduced ship draft. In addition, they offer simplicity, low cost, easy maintenance and elimination of complex power transmission gearing systems. Also, by rotating the jet discharge, it is possible that water jets can be made directional, either for steering, turning or even slowing down. If the tests confirm this theory, CAB ships using jet propulsion will not need rudders!

In summary, the CAB promises to fill the gap which now exists between the slow, conventional, low-freight-cost cargo ship (under 25 knots) and the high speed (above 200 knots) high-freight-cost airplane.

It is the ship of tomorrow.

11

The Hydrofoils—Ships
That Fly in Water

Up to this point, we have been discussing boats and ships which "fly" in the air—the air cushion vehicles and captured air bubble ships. As I have stated earlier, there is a third type of flying ship which actually flies *in* (not above) the water—the hydrofoil. We learned in Chapter 1 that, to make a ship go much faster than 35 knots, it must be lifted out of the water and into the air, where the resistance is 815 times less than in water. All the "its" that we have discussed so far have used air pressure to raise their hulls out of water, completely or in part, by blowing air under pressure beneath the hull, and holding or trapping it there by some means. The hydrofoil, on the other hand, uses underwater wings, called hydrofoils, which create lift, just as an airplane's wings create lift. In the hydrofoil, the fluid medium is water; for the airplane, it is air.

What is the appeal of the hydrofoil? First of all, it is faster than an ordinary boat. Second, it offers a more comfortable ride.

Hydrofoils are much older than either ACV's or CAB's. In fact, they are older than airplanes!

The first hydrofoil was demonstrated in France, in the Seine

The five-ton Ladder Hydrofoil of Alexander Graham Bell and Casey Baldwin, built in 1918

River, by Count Alexander de Lambert, in 1891. The next significant work was done on Lake Maggiore, in Italy, in 1906, by Enrico Forlanini, who built and demonstrated a 40-knot hydrofoil.

Even Wilbur and Orville Wright were engaged in an attempt to build a hydrofoil before they started on airplanes!

And the inventor of the telephone, Dr. Alexander Graham Bell, in cooperation with Mr. Frederick W. (Casey) Baldwin, designed and built a 5-ton ladder-type hydrofoil called the HD-4, in 1918. Powered by two 350-horsepower Liberty aircraft engines, it is reported to have reached a speed of 70.86 miles an hour! (See Figure 57.) (Bell's project never received government support. If it had, those rum-runners of the 1920's would have been in deep trouble!)

During World War II, the Germans became very interested in hydrofoils and designed and built a number of them. None, however, found any military use. The principal German designer was Baron Hanns Von Schertel. Quite a few of the passenger-carrying hydrofoils in use today were designed by Baron Schertel, and many look upon him as the father of modern commercial hydrofoils.

Types of Hydrofoils.

There are three principal types of hydrofoils which can be distinguished by the kinds of foils or "wings" they use. The first is the *surface piercing foil*, so named because the tips of its foils usually stick up above the surface of the water. Hydrofoils of this type are very sensitive to waves, and in rough water, a passenger's ride can be quite uncomfortable. But in sheltered waters, and in rivers, they are quite comfortable and fast and a great many such hydrofoils are in operation today. They are inherently stable and have the advantage of not requiring costly computer-controlled systems.

The second type is a variation of the surface piercing foil—the *ladder type foil*. As the name implies, this foil involves a strut with several steps or foils at various heights.

The third basic type of hydrofoil is the *fully submerged foil*. Boats with these foils operate with their foils completely submerged at all times, and hence are much less sensitive to waves and rough water. In these, the craft stays fairly level while the water below it rises and falls. (See Figure 58.)

In a sense, therefore, the hydrofoil is a blending of the high-speed boat and the airplane. When you ride a hydrofoil for the first time,

Three types of Hydrofoil Ships

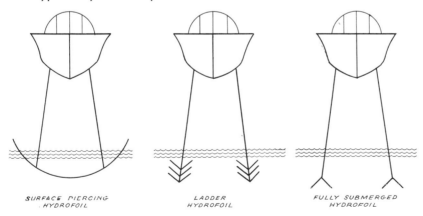

SURFACE PIERCING HYDROFOIL   LADDER HYDROFOIL   FULLY SUBMERGED HYDROFOIL

you get the sensation of flying. I recall my first ride, which is fairly typical. We moved away from the pier and through the harbor, rolling gently and moving as in any ordinary boat.

But once outside the harbor, and the power was advanced, the ship picked up speed, shuddering and vibrating a little . . . then, suddenly—just as is the case with an airplane when its wheels clear the ground—the vibration and noise disappeared, followed by that smooth sensation of being airborne and out of touch with the ground—flying on a hydrofoil!

How Does a Hydrofoil Work

There are two main shapes which the "foils" or wings of a hydrofoil can take. The first is the conventional aircraft wing or elongated teardrop shape—such foils are called "sub-cavitating" foils. The second shape is a special thin wedge-shaped foil which is called a "super-cavitating" foil. Figure 59 shows the difference.

These sub-cavitating foils, which are shaped like elongated tear drops, or the crossection of an airplane wing, have an economical top speed of about 50 to 60 knots. At speeds up to this limit, both the upper and lower sides of the foil remain wet. In other words,

Types of Foils—Subcavitating and Supercavitating

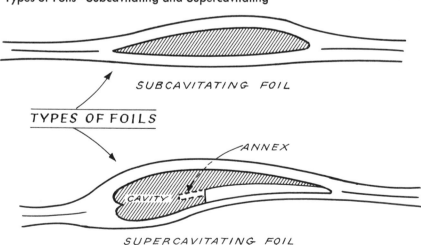

TYPES OF FOILS

the water always touches both surfaces. Lift is obtained in the same manner as the airplane gets its lift, by a difference in pressure—higher pressure *below* the foil, decreased pressure *above* the foil, hence an upward *lift*, caused by the movement of the foil or wing through the fluid—in this case, water.

But when such a foil shape is driven through water at speeds greater than 50-60 knots, small bubbles or "cavities" are formed on the low-pressure or upper side of the foil, which is detrimental to performance and damaging to the foil itself.

For many years, marine engineers did not know how to solve this problem. In many ways, it was like trying to get an airplane through the sound barrier. The answer was finally found in changing the shape of the foil to a very thin, narrow, wedge-shaped "wing."

As stated above, the super-cavitating foil produces a very large cavity behind the foil, which collapses and is *not* corrosive to the foil itself. Moreover, when it is pushed through water at high speeds, only the lower, or *bottom* side of the foil is always wet.

This type of foil can be driven through the water to speeds as high as 90 knots, and it is the type which the high-speed hydrofoils of tomorrow will use.

Present Hydrofoil Commercial Applications

Although the hydrofoil goes back to 1891, is was not until 1953 that the first passenger service by hydrofoil was inaugurated—in Lake Maggiore, between Switzerland and Italy—using a Supramar PT-10 craft which would carry 32 passengers. And it was not until the late 1950's that serious naval interest in hydrofoils became evident.

The last few years, however, have seen the hydrofoil forge strongly ahead, in the commercial ferry and short-haul passenger business, in naval affairs, and, to a lesser extent, in sporting craft. It has been estimated that thirty-five million passengers have traveled by hydrofoil.

Typical of the hydrofoil ferry routes now in existence are those services between Seattle, Washington, and Victoria, B.C.; between

The Soviet hydrofoil, *Kometa*, carries 100 passengers at 32-35 knots

Naples, Italy, and the Island of Capri; from Messina to Reggio, in Calabria; Southampton, England to Cowes, Isle of Wight; Hong Kong to Macao and the New Territories; around the Canary Islands, and Denmark and Norway. Russian hydrofoils operate between Yalta and Sevastopol, Leningrad and Tallin, Gorki and Moscow, Odessa and Batum, and in most of her main rivers and canals. In fact, Russia probably leads the world in hydrofoil passenger traffic. (See Figure 60.) Since many of her major cities are situated on large rivers and her road network is poorly developed, Russia has concentrated on inter-city travel, and operates about 300 hydrofoils over 137 routes. Other services by hydrofoil are in Trinidad and Grenada, a service in Poland; a 4 hour, 40 minute service between Vienna and Budapest in the Danube River. In Japan there are 25 hydrofoils in service, including inter-island ones through the Inland Sea. Australia and New Zealand are starting hydrofoil services. Eleven hydrofoils are in operation in South America, many serving offshore oil drilling rigs. There are, in fact, more than 500 hydrofoils operating in ferry runs at the present time. This number will double in ten years.

The biggest commercial hydrofoil in operation at the present

The PT 150 *Expressan,* is the world's biggest commercial hydrofoil

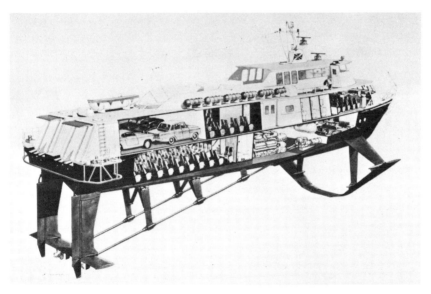

The interior arrangements of *Expressan.* Normal seating is 120-155 passengers

time is the PT 150 *Expressan,* a 123 foot long, 165-ton craft which cruises at approximately 35 knots and can carry either 250 passengers or 150 passengers and 8 automobiles. (See Figures 61 and 62.)

Designed by Baron Von Schertel, this air stabilized hydrofoil is serving Frederikshavn, Gothenburg and Aalberg in the Kattegat, between Sweden and Denmark. (On the Gothenburg-Frederikshavn route, the conventional ferryboat run was reduced from four hours to one hour and forty minutes.) This ship is typical of the medium-sized ocean-going hydrofoils which will be used increasingly in the future.

One feature of the hydrofoil which makes it so convenient for passengers is its ability to slow down and stop in three ship lengths—and smoothly. Unlike the hovercraft, winds and drift are no problem. Riding on the foils, hydrofoils produce little wake—another advantage in a harbor where damaging waves are discouraged.

Naval Applications

The argument is heard frequently that the naval ships a generation hence will be smaller, faster, more specialized and with a reduced crew. Why operate big, expensive cruisers, the argument goes, when you can have a whole fleet of small, fast, hard hitting hydrofoils for the same money? Those who favor this idea say that many small ships could have equal or greater hitting power than a single cruiser, but would be much less vulnerable to either air or guided missile attack.

The author is not ready to buy this idea, but it is one of the persuasive arguments that nations with small navies, long coastlines, and limited resources are hearing more often. The sinking of the Israeli destroyer, *Elath*, off Alexandria by an Egyptian PT missile boat in 1966 is mentioned in evidence.

In any case, the high speeds of the hydrofoils—40 knots today, double that tomorrow, with these high speeds even in rough water —have given new impetus to their use in anti-submarine warfare and short range strike roles.

There are other promised advantages for hydrofoils—a stable gun or missile platform, better than average sea-keeping ability, and a small operating crew.

There are four U.S. Navy ships already in experimental use which will point the way to how the hydrofoils will develop—the gunboat *Flagstaff* (PGH-1) (*Patrol Gunboat Hydrofoil*), the gunboat *Tucumcari* (PGH-2) (*Patrol Gunboat Hydrofoil*), the *Plainview* (AGEH-1) (Auxiliary General Experimental Hydrofoil), the world's largest hydrofoil, and *Highpoint* (PCH-1) (*Patrol Craft Hydrofoil*).

The *Flagstaff* and *Tucumcari* are approximately the same size— 73 feet long and 65 tons, 70 feet long and 55 tons respectively. The principal differences are in the foil arrangements and the power plants.

The *Flagstaff* (built by Grumman) carries her weight supported 70 per cent on the two forward foils and only 30 per cent on the tail foil. When flying on her foils, she is powered by a 3600 horse-power gas turbine, driving a super-cavitating controlled pitch propeller. When hullborne, she is powered by two 320 horsepower diesels.

The *Tucumcari* (built by Boeing) carries 30 per cent of her

The **USS** *Tucumcari,* a patrol boat hydrofoil, is the first of a new breed of fast fighting ships

weight on a single bow foil and 70 per cent on her two after foils. Her power plant is a 3200 horsepower gas turbine but the propulsion is water jet. (See Figure 63.)

The *Highpoint* (built by Boeing) is 115 feet long and displaces 117 tons. She has one foil forward which carries 30 per cent of her weight and an inverted foil aft which carries 70 per cent of her weight. She is powered by two 3,100 HP gas turbines which drive two tandem sets of propellers (one tractor, one pusher per set). The *Plainview* and *Highpoint* are engaged in basic hydrofoil research at Bremerton, Washington.

The *Plainview* (built by Lockheed) is the largest hydrofoil now in existence—320 tons. She has two main foils forward, which carry 90 per cent of her weight. The remainder rests on the aft foil. She is 320 feet long and powered by two gas turbines which provide 14,000 horsepower to drive the two super-cavitating propellers. Space has been provided so that two additional gas turbines can be added at a later time, to achieve speeds as high as 90 knots.

One minor disadvantage with hydrofoils should be mentioned. If they have fixed foils, they require the ship to have a deeper draft; if they do not, they require some mechanism to raise them out of the water.

One of the few hydrofoils that you can buy. It is made by Wynne-Gill of Miami, Florida. This craft can seat four people.

The Hi-Foil, a personal English hydrofoil, made by Anglican Development Limited on the Isle of Wight. It seats two and has motorcycle steering.

The Future

What does the future hold for the hydrofoil?

Most experts agree that, for the next decade, hydrofoils are size-limited—and will grow to no more than about 1000 tons. This means that commercial operations will be confined largely to inland river or protected waterways—not open-ocean work.

There will be additional hydrofoil growth in the sports field. Figures 64 and 65 are two typical small hydrofoils which can be purchased.

In the naval field, the future is not as clear. Certainly, the hydrofoil offers a stable platform at high speed. But for the present there is insufficient range capability to permit really open-ocean, large size hydrofoils. Their capability will best be used as fast patrol craft near the coastline.

The hydrofoils and hovercraft are not competitive—there is a place for each. The next generation will certainly see tremendous growth in hydrofoil development and use.

12

The Future of
Flying Ships

There is little doubt that the world is witnessing the opening scene of a major revolutionary drama in transportation, and that the earth's oceans, which cover 70 per cent of our globe, will see some great changes during the next 25 to 50 years. While the huge jumbo jets and the supersonic jet transports (SST) will make vast changes in air travel, ACV's, hydrofoils and CAB's (using nuclear power, gas turbine, and jet propulsion) will make equally vast changes in maritime affairs. And the impact on naval forces promises to be equally momentous.

To summarize and expand on what has been stated before, the first area of marine travel to be affected will be the protected-water ferry and commuter services. As noted in Chapter 6, there is hardly a big city in the world which is not on a waterway or river, and most of them are now suffering from automobile congestion. Part of this congestion can be relieved by the ACV hovercraft of which Figures 66 and 67 are typical examples and which point the way to the future.

There are a number of commuter and short-haul ferry services

The river and inland waterway ACV can help find the answer to the problem of city congestion

The *Swift*, now in service between England and France, is another solution to the crowded commuter problem. It can travel to the heart of city areas on lakes or rivers.

already running and this number will increase every year. Several of these services are now operating in England, and others are running or planned for Puget Sound, the Bahamas, Holland, the Gulf of Taranto, the Greek islands of the Ionian Sea, Gibraltar-Tangiers, Copenhagen-Oslo, the Cote d'Azur, and the Irish Sea. As experience is gained, and more ACV's are built, this commuter and short-haul ferry service will certainly increase.

The second area of great promise for ACV service will be in the underdeveloped areas of the continents of Africa and South America, and in many of the semipolar, snow-covered areas of the globe. Already, tests have been made by ACV's in such areas as the Amazon, Faulkland Islands, Rio Negro and Orinoco. Canada has done extensive research in her northern provinces where snow is a seven-months-per-year problem. In the southern hemisphere, as stated earlier, hovercraft will permit rivers to be used for highways into the hinterlands of countries which have no highways. The ACV's can carry freight and passengers and provide the necessary services in the absence of modern highways much more cheaply than it would cost to build a network of roads. The delta regions of the tropics will be particularly appealing for hovercraft service.

The third sphere to be greatly changed by ACV's and CAB's will be the United States Navy—and perhaps other navies.

The first naval mission to be affected will be amphibious warfare. Hovercraft will make more of a potential enemy's coastline vulnerable to amphibious attack. Until now, a nation's seacoast could be considered secure if only those ideal beaches which were clear of obstacles, shoals, sandbars, and coral reefs were defended. With amphibious ACV's, however, any coastal terrain which is reasonably flat and clear of trees, no matter how difficult the sea approaches, will be vulnerable to ACV's. The lowlands, mud flats, rice paddies, and marshlands which, throughout history, have been considered safe from enemy invasion will be safe no more. Moreover, underwater obstacles and minefields off the good beaches will not stop the ACV's. A whole new dimension for amphibious warfare is opened up, especially if one can have a 60-knot force of CAB

An artist's conception of ACV's being used in a swift amphibious assault on an enemy beach. The Bell SK-10 will carry Marines and their equipment at speeds up to 80 knots. It can carry a main battle tank or up to 500 troops.

transport ships loaded with U.S. Marines who come ashore from the CAB's in ACV's. The possibilities here are enormous, and the Leathernecks are eager to use them.

An amphibious assault, for example, could be made in a radically different manner from what is now traditional. Instead of massing a fleet of slow-moving amphibious ships and Landing Ships (LST's), the amphibious attack could consist of a number of 60-knot CAB's converging from many different directions on an enemy objective at high speed and making the final across-the-beach attack from smaller, troop-carrying ACV's, transported inside the CAB's. Once the Marines are landed, the ACV's would then shuttle the logistic support from other ships well out at sea. Such an amphibious assault would be swift, hard to detect and difficult to defeat—either by submarines, mines, or beach defenses. (See Figure 68.)

The next naval field which will feel the impact of the ACV is mine warfare. An ACV operating over the surface of the sea makes only the smallest acoustic, magnetic and pressure signature. It is, therefore, relatively invulnerable to mines. Moreover, the ACV has promise of being useful as a minesweeper.

The third area of naval warfare to be affected will be that of anti-submarine warfare (ASW). Torpedoes will be almost useless against an ACV flying above the sea or against a CAB whose high speed draft is only a few feet—especially one which is making more than 60 knots.

Today, nuclear powered submarines are faster than both the hunter and the hunted. For twenty years, they have enjoyed a speed advantage over most conventional combat ships. But ship designers acknowledge that the upper practical speed limit for a nuclear submarine is about 50 knots. Thus, with many naval ships of the future able to run at speeds much higher than 50 knots, the nuclear powered submarine will lose its speed advantage. Submarines will have a more difficult problem of attacking and sinking an ocean-going

The Bell SK-10, as pictured here, can also carry a main battle tank or up to 500 troops

CAB which is moving at 60-100 knots and drawing only several inches of water, especially with 50-knot torpedoes. CAB's, ACV's, and hydrofoils will be faster than the torpedo itself!

The CAB destroyer will also have a greater advantage with which to challenge the security of the elusive nuclear submarine. It would be capable of using a variety of detection and classification devices; it would be able to lie quietly and search a suspicious area, then move at 100 knots (faster than the submarine) to his immediate area and attack. Finally, it would carry an assortment of weapons to attack the submarine.

Insofar as major combatants are concerned, being able to move CAB aircraft carriers and CAB missile cruisers at speeds of 60-80 or even 100 knots will introduce a tremendous new range of naval opportunity and potential. In combination with vertical take-off aircraft, which are already flying, the strategic and tactical advantages which will accrue to such a Navy are boundless.

CAB aircraft carriers moving at 60-80 knots, and eventually at 100 knots, would not need the catapult launching and arresting gear used today, since the speed of the landing or departing aircraft would match that of the ship. Aircraft could be launched directly from the elevators.

Such carriers could move from one ocean area to another in far less time than has been possible heretofore.

Today's typical carrier task force can be as large as 30 ships. The author commanded such a force in 1969. With 3 or 4 carriers, 4 cruisers and 22 destroyers, moving at 25 to 30 knots, such an assembly has great self-defense. One of the ships is an ASW carrier with airplanes and helicopters for hunting and sinking submarines. On every ship there are electronic warfare devices and, on each of the big flattops, special EW aircraft which are designed to detect and defeat incoming enemy missiles. Also on the carriers are many fighters, while the cruisers and destroyers are armed with missiles which can defeat incoming enemy bombing aircraft. Such a fleet represents awesome striking power. But it is true that such a fleet is

Painting of the one-hundred-knot, 5000- to 10,000-ton freighter of the future
—the ocean-going CAB. Propulsion may eventually be nuclear.

With only a fifteen-man crew, a 4,000-ton CAB will be able to cross the
Atlantic in thirty-six hours, at an average cruising speed on 80 knots.

an expensive one and that a good fraction of its strength is for defensive purposes.

The 100-knot ships of tomorrow's navy will radically change this picture and diminish that fraction of power which is defensive in purpose. More of the power of a 100-knot fleet could be offensive. There would be reduced need for submarine defenses, missile defenses, and aircraft defenses, because a fleet moving at 100 knots is far less vulnerable than a fleet moving at 25 knots. Speed itself is a great protection.

But a word of caution is wise at this point. Neither a 100-knot merchant fleet nor a 100-knot navy will come quickly or cheaply. The cost will be enormous and many problems—some now unforeseen—will be discovered by the test vehicles now being built. All these will have to be overcome. There can be no doubt that the progress and advances made to date are remarkable, nor can there be any doubt that 100-knot ocean-going ships are achievable. The process of getting from where we are today to that bright day of tomorrow will not come as easily and cheaply, or as quickly and simply as some writers have indicated. But it *will* come.

One of the many unknowns for the future is ship size itself. In 1970, the ship design experts talk about CAB ships as large as 12,500 tons. Presently, we have combat ships which exceed 85,000 tons, and oil transport ships exceeding 300,000 tons. But will there be any real need for such large but slow ships in the world of tomorrow? Might not several, high speed, 100 knot ships of the 5,000-10,000 ton capacity be more useful and less expensive than super-sized CAB's? It is too early yet to predict that CAB's will replace the huge conventional ships—but it *is* certain that there is a real need and market for the high speed, 5 to 10 thousand ton cargo ship.

The final area of marine endeavor is that of ocean commerce. This, perhaps, will undergo the greatest change of all. In Chapter 10, we discussed the CAB cargo ship in some detail. This ocean-going CAB will open up an entirely new market that is still untouched. (See Figure 69.)

The automobile has urbanized many nations and demolished state boundaries and distance considerations. People have moved off the farms and into the cities. In a similar manner, the airplane shrank the globe and the tourist industry boomed.

Just so, the high speed CAB ship of the 1980's and 1990's will produce changes as great as those brought about by either the automobile or the airplane. The CAB ship is the ideal transportation platform for the automated, prepackaged, roll-on, roll-off type of cargo that has recently been developed. A fleet of CAB ships can carry the merchandise of the world's trading nations both faster and easier than conventional cargo ships. (See Figures 70 and 71.)

The high speed, ocean-going CAB will revolutionize all aspects of the shipping industry. The methods and materials of ship construction will be affected and ships of tomorrow will be built by processes more closely resembling those used in the aircraft industry. Probably the aircraft construction industry and the ship construction industry will be merged. The packaging, handling, loading, and discharging of freight will be changed, forcing modernization of old fashioned, slow-speed methods of cargo handling. The problems of maintenance repair and overhaul of CAB ships will be vastly different from any methods known today. And the traditional ways of manning ships will be drastically changed. As pointed out before,

The general arrangement of a CAB planned for the 1980 period. It will be able to handle pre-packaged roll-on, roll-off cargo.

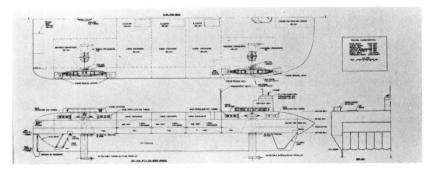

The passenger-carrying open-ocean CAB ship of tomorrow, will be able to cross lakes, seas and oceans at 100 knots. The diagram shows the general arrangement.

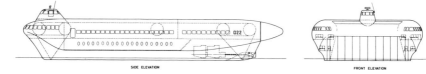

SIDE ELEVATION

FRONT ELEVATION

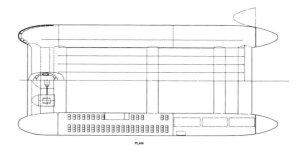

GENERAL ARRANGEMENT OF
HOVERMARINE HM.4 PROJECT

PLAN

crew requirements will be less, not only because of faster trips, but also because the manning requirements for gas turbine propulsion and lift systems will be less than for the conventional ships' steam plants. The 10,000-ton CAB cargo ship might have only a ten to fifteen man crew. Moreover, automation will be fully utilized in these ships, further reducing manpower requirements. (See Figures 72a and 72b.)

As for the tourist trade, the CAB passenger ship of tomorrow will cross the Atlantic in thirty-six hours. This will make it possible for an American family on a two-week holiday to motor to an East Coast port, drive aboard a CAB ship, arrive in Europe in 30-40 hours, have a week's motoring holiday on the continent, and be home again before the average two weeks of vacation are up.

In summary, we stand at the threshold of a transportation revolution which will change the face of the world. And it will come so quickly that you who read this book will not only watch it happen —but may also help to bring it about. Undoubtedly, you will share profitably and pleasurably in its achievements.

Manufacturers of Sporting ACV's and ACV Kits

1. "HOVERSPRAY" (Canada)	Air Cushion System Consultants Suite 25, 15 Esterbrooke Ave. Willowdale, Ontario, Canada	$2296 for complete kit; $3094 assembled craft, ready to operate. (Plans only $30.)
2. "POWER BREEZE" (U.S.A.)	POWER BREEZE Department HW 8139 Matilija Panorama City, Calif. 91402	$5.00 drawings and parts list only.
3. "FAN JET SKIMMER" (England)	AIRHOVER LIMITED Mill Dam Lake St. Osyth, Essex, England	$600 or £178 for kit (less engine). $1200 or £248 for completed vehicle.
(U.S.A.)	SKIMMERS, INC. P.O. Box 855 Severna Park, Md. 21146	
4. "HOVERSCOUT" (England)	HOVERKNIGHTS 95 Rickmansworth Road Pinner, Middlesex, England	Two HOVERCRAFT kits (less engine) 6 x 11 ft., £30; 7 x 14 ft., £40.
5. "HOVERHAWK" (England)	HOVER-AIR LTD Crowland, Peterborough, U.K.	Approximate cost FOB £1595.
"HOVERHORNET" (UK)	HOVER-AIR LTD Crowland, Peterborough, U.K.	Kit for an 8 x 7 ACV, £370.
6. "DOBSON AIR CAR MODEL D" (U.S.A.)	DOBSON PRODUCTS CO. 4518 Roxbury Road Corona Del Mar, Calif. 92625	Kit less engine $685 (£286). Factory built $2395 (£1000).
7. "REVFLITE" (U.S.A.)	REVMASTER, INC. 930 North Main Street Riverside, Calif. 92501	$2995 (£1250).
8. "FLEETWING ARROW" (UK)	HOVERSPARES LTD 24 Albert Road Levenshulme, Manchester, U.K.	£750 in fiberglass, £499 in plywood.

9. "CRESTED WREN" (UK)

Barwren, Hover LTD
Diamond Road
Whitstable, Kent, U.K.

£1285 plus £85 packing and delivery to dock charges.

10. "FLYING SAUCER"

BARTLETT FLYING SAUCER
Box 3234
Scottsdale, Arizona 85257

Prices not available for a one passenger ACV, either in kit form or plans only.

11. "SMUGGLER" (USA)

AIR KINETICS, INC.
5555 NW 5th Street
Miami, Florida 33126

Two seat, amphibious fiberglass ACV powered by a VW engine. Prices not available.

HATTON & BASS LTD
43 South Audley Street
London WI, England

Glossary of ACV and Hydrofoil Terms

*ACV—Air cushion vehicle—*A vehicle capable of being operated so that its weight, including its payload, is wholly or significantly supported on a continuously generated cushion or "bubble" of air at higher than ambient pressure. The air bubble or cushion is put under pressure by a fan or fans and generally contained beneath the vehicle's structure by flexible skirts or sidewalls. In the United States large or ship-size air cushion vehicles are called surface effect ships.

*Air Gap—*Also called daylight gap, daylight clearance and hover gap. Distance between the lowest component of the vehicle's understructure, e.g., skirt hem, and the surface when riding on its cushion. *Air Gap Area.* Area through which air is able to leak from a cushion.

*Air Pallet—*Also called hover pallet and other trade names. Air cushion-supported, load-carrying structure, which bleeds a continuous low pressure volume of air between the structure and the reaction surface, creating an air film.

*CAB—Captured Air Bubble—*Vessel in which the cushion (or air bubble) is contained by rigid sidewalls and flexible bow and stern skirts. Occasionally used for any air cushion craft in which the air cushion (or air bubble) is contained within the cushion periphery with minimal air leakage.

*Cavitation—*The formation and collapse of vapor bubbles due to pressure decrease on the upper surface of a foil or the back of a propeller's blades at high speeds. Cavitation bubbles form near the foil's leading edge and extend downstream, expanding and collapsing. At the points of collapse positive pressure peaks may rise to as high as 20,000 psi. These cause corrosion and pitting of the metal. Cavitation causes an unstable water flow over the foils which results in abrupt changes in lift and therefore discomfort for those aboard the craft.

Foil sections are now being developed which either delay the onset of cavitation by reduced camber, thinner sections, or sweepback, or, if the craft is required to operate at supercavitating speeds, provide a smooth transition between sub-cavitating and super-cavitating speeds.

Centrifugal Flow Lift Fan—A cushion lift fan which generates an airflow at right angles to the axis of rotation.

Craft—Boats, ships, air cushion vehicles and hydrofoils of all types, regardless of size.

Cushion—A volume of higher than ambient pressure air trapped beneath the structure of a vehicle and its supporting surface causing the vehicle to be supported at some distance from the ground.

Cushion-Borne—A craft borne above the sea or land surface by its air cushion.

Cushion Seal—Air curtains, sidewalls, skirts, water-jets or other means employed to contain or seal an air cushion to reduce to a minimum the leakage of trapped air.

Daylight Clearance—See *air gap*.

Drag—(1) ACV's—aerodynamic and hydrodynamic resistances encountered by an air cushion vehicle resulting from aerodynamic profile, gain of momentum of air needed for cushion generation, wave making, wetting or skirt contact.

(2) Hydrofoils—hydrodynamic resistances encountered by hydrofoils result from wave making, which is dependent on the craft shape and displacement, frictional drag due to the viscosity of the water, the total foils and transmission shafts and their supporting struts and structure, due to their motion through the water.

Ferry—A craft designed to carry passengers across a channel, estuary, lake, river or strait.

Finger Skirt—See *Skirts*.

Flexible Skirt—See *skirts*.

Foilborne—A hydrofoil is said to be foilborne when the hull is raised completely out of the water and wholly supported by lift from its foil system.

Foil Flaps—Foils are frequently fitted with (a) trailing edge flaps for lift augmentation during take-off and to provide control forces, (b) upper and lower flaps to raise the cavitation boundary.

Ladder Foils—These come under the heading of *surface piercing*, but are rarely used at the present time. This was used by Forlanini in his 1905 hydro-aeroplane, the first really successful hydrofoil. In 1911, Alexander Graham Bell purchased Forlanini's patent specifications and used his ladder system on his Hydrodrome, one of which, the HD-4, set up a world speed record of 61.5 knots in 1919.

Submerged Foils—These have a greater potential for seakeeping than any other, but are not inherently stable. The foils are totally immersed and a stabilization system has to be installed to maintain the foils at the required depth. The system has to stabilize the craft from take-off to touchdown in all four axes—pitch, roll, yaw and heave. It must also see that the craft makes coordinated banked turns in heavy seas to reduce the side loads on the foil struts, ensure that vertical and lateral accelerations are kept within limits in order to prevent excessive loads on the structure and, finally, ensure a smooth ride for the passengers and crew.

The control forces are generated either by deflecting flaps at the trailing edge of the foil or varying the incidence angle of the entire foil surface. Incidence control provides better performance in a high sea state.

A typical sonic electronic autopilot control system is that devised for the Boeing High Point PGH-1. The key element is an acoustic height sensor located at the bow. The time lag of the return signal is a measure of the distance of the sensor from the water.

Craft motion input is received from dual sonic ranging devices which sense the height above the water of the bow in relation to a fixed reference; from three rate gyros which measure yaw, pitch and roll; from forward and aft accelerometers which sense vertical acceleration fore and aft and from a vertical gyro which senses the angular position of the craft in both pitch and roll. This information is processed by an electronic computer and fed continuously to hydraulic actuators of the foil control surfaces, which develop the necessary hydrodynamic forces for stability producing forces imposed by wave action maneuvering and correct flight.

Surface Piercing Foils—These are more often than not vee-shaped, the upper parts of the foil forming the tips of the Vee and piercing the surface on either side of the craft. The vee foil, with its marked dihedral is area stabilized and craft employing this configuration can be designed to be inherently stable, and, for stability, geometry dependent.

The forces restoring normal trim are provided by the area of the foil that is submerged. A roll to one side means the immersion of increased foil area, which results in the generation of extra lift to counter the roll and restore the craft to an even keel.

Equally, a downward pitching movement at the bow means an increase in the submerged area of the forward foil, and the generation of extra lift on this foil, which raises the bow once more. Should the bow foil rise above its normal water level, the lift decreases in a similar way to restore normal trim. This type of foil is also known as an *emerging foil system.*

As the vee-foil craft increases its speed, so it generates greater lift and is raised further out of the water—at the same time reducing the wetted area and the lift. The lift must be equal to the weight of the craft, and as the lift depends on the speed and wetted foil area, the hull rides at a pre-determined height above the water level.

Full Hover—Expression used to describe the condition of an ACV when it is at its design hoverheight.

GEM—Ground effect machine—Early generic term for air cushion vehicles of all types.

Hover Commander—Senior crew member aboard a hovercraft. Equivalent in rank to airliner or ship's captain. Alternative terms: pilot, driver, captain, helmsman and coxswain.

Hovercraft—Generic name for craft using the patented peripheral jet principle invented by Christopher Cockerell, CBE, in which the air cushion is generated and contained by a jet of air exhausted downward and inward from a nozzle at the periphery at the base of the vehicle.

Hover Height—Vertical height between the hard structure of an ACV and the supporting surface when a vehicle is cushion-borne.

Hover Pallet—See *air pallet.*

Hump—The "hump" formed on the graph of resistance against the speed of a displacement vessel or ACV. The maximum of the "hump" corresponds to the speed of the wave generated by the hull or air depression.

Hump Speed—Critical speed at which the curve on a graph of wave making drag of an ACV tends to hump or peak. As speed is increased, the craft over-rides its bow wave, the wave-making drag diminishes and the rate of acceleration rapidly increases.

Hydrofoils—Small wings, almost identical in section to those of an aircraft, and designed to generate lift. Since water has a density some 815 times that of air, the same lift as an airplane wing is obtained for only 1/815 of the area (at equal speeds).

Hydroskimmer—Name given originally to experimental air cushion vehicles built under contract to the US Navy Bureau of Ships. Preference was given to this name since it bestowed on the craft a sea-service identity.

Knot—A nautical mile per hour.

Nautical Mile—A distance of 6,080 feet, or one minute of latitude at the equator.

Peripheral Jet—See *AIR CURTAIN* and *HOVERCRAFT*.

Peripheral Jet Cushion System—A ground cushion generated by a continuous jet of air issued through ducts or nozzles around the outer periphery of the base of a craft. The cushion is maintained at above ambient pressure by the horizontal change of momentum of the curtain.

Plenum—Space or air chamber beneath or surrounding a lift fan or fans through which air under pressure is distributed to a skirt system.

Plenum Chamber Cushion System—The most simple of air cushion concepts. Cushion pressure is maintained by pumping air continuously into a recessed base without the use of a peripheral jet curtain.

Puff Ports—Controlled apertures in a skirt system or cushion supply ducting through which air can be expelled to assist control at low speeds.

SES—See *Surface Effect Ship*.

Sidewall Vessel—An ACV with its cushion air contained between immersed sidewalls or skegs and transverse air curtains or skirts fore and aft. Stability is provided by the buoyancy of the sidewalls and their planing forces.

Skirt—Flexible fabric extension hung between an ACV's metal structure and the surface to give increased obstacle and overwave clearance capability for a small air gap clearance and therefore reduced power requirement. The skirt deflects when encountering waves or solid obstacles, then returns to its normal position, the air gap being increased only momentarily. On peripheral jet ACV's the skirt is a flexible extension of the peripheral jet nozzle with inner and outer skins hung from the inner and outer edges of the air duct and linked together by chain ties or diaphragms so that they form the correct nozzle profile at the hemline.

Skirt, Bag—Simple skirt design consisting of an inflated bag. Sometimes used as traverse and longitudinal stability skirts.

Skirt, Finger—Skirt system designed by Hovercraft Development Ltd., consisting of a fringe of conically shaped nozzles attached to the base of a bag or loop skirt. Each nozzle or finger fits around an air exit hole and channels cushion air inward toward the bottom center of the craft. The most successful skirt design developed so far, it produces substantially less drag through surface contact in calm water and wave conditions and also reduces the amount of spray normally generated by cushion air by about 75 per cent.

Submerged Foil System—A foil system employing totally submerged lifting surfaces. The depth of submergence is controlled by mechanical, electronic or pneumatic systems which alter the angle of incidence of the foils or flaps attached to them to provide stability and control. See *foil systems*.

Supercavitating Foil—A general classification given to foils designed to operate efficiently at high speeds while fully cavitated. Since at very high speeds foils cannot avoid cavitation, sections are being designed which induce the onset of cavitation from the leading edge and cause the cavities to proceed downstream and beyond the trailing edge before collapsing. Lift and drag of these foils is determined by the shape of the leading edge and undersurface.

Surface Effect Ship—Term implying a large ship-size ACV, regardless of specific type.

Take-Off Speed—Speed at which the hull of a hydrofoil craft is raised clear of the water, dynamic foil lift taking over from static displacement or planing of the hull proper.

Tandem Foils—Foil system in which the area of the forward foils is approximately equal to that of the aft foils, balancing the loading between them.

Trapped Air Cushion Vehicle—A concept for a skirt-type surface effect ship with 20-foot skirts separated from the water surface by a thin film of air lubrication.

Waterjet Propulsion—A term now applied to a propulsion system devised as an alternative to supercavitating propellers for propelling high speed ship systems. Turbines drive pumps located in the hull, and water is pumped through high velocity jets above the water line and directed astern. The system weighs less than a comparable supercavitating propeller system, and for craft with normal operating speeds above 45 knots it is thought to be competitive on an annual cost basis. The jet can be turned easily to give side propulsion to facilitate docking which is not so easy for a normal propeller.

Index

139

Rear Admiral
Malcolm W. Cagle, U.S.N.

is a native of Tennessee. He graduated from Annapolis in 1941, a few months before Pearl Harbor. He spent two years on a destroyer in the North Atlantic before going through naval aviation flight training at Pensacola. During the last year of World War II, he served as commanding officer of Fighting Squadron 88, aboard *USS Yorktown*, in the Western Pacific. Because of his outstanding World War II service, he won the Navy Cross, the Distinguished Flying Cross, and the Air Medal. Later, he commanded Fighting Squadron 63 in the Atlantic Fleet.

Admiral Cagle also served in the Korean War and, based upon that experience, wrote *The Sea War in Korea*, in addition to collaborating with the late Walter Karig in writing *Battle Report*. In 1960, he was Deputy Director of the Institute of Naval Studies, a civilian "think tank," in Cambridge, Massachusetts.

In 1963, Admiral Cagle commanded the *USS Suribachi*, a fleet ammunition ship, and in 1964, he took command of the aircraft carrier *Franklin D. Roosevelt*. Promoted to Rear Admiral in 1966, he made two deployments to the Gulf of Tonkin as Commander Carrier Division One, flying his flag aboard the nuclear powered carrier *Enterprise*. It was during this period that he served as Commander Task Force 71 in operations in the Sea of Japan, following the destruction of an American reconnaissance airplane by the North Koreans. For this service, Admiral Cagle was awarded the Distinguished Service Medal. He is presently functioning as the Navy's Director of General Plans and Programs in the Pentagon.

In addition to his military service, Admiral Cagle has done extensive writing and has four other books to his credit, including FLYING SHIPS: HOVERCRAFT AND HYDROFOILS. He also owns a 320 acre farm in Nelson County, Virginia.

This photograph of Admiral Cagle was taken on the Flag Bridge of the *USS Enterprise* where he sat to watch air operations and flight movements in general while he was Commander of Task Force 71, operating in the Pacific.